Your Ham Antenna Companion

By Paul Danzer, N1II

Published by: **The American Radio Relay League**
225 Main Street, Newington, CT 06111-1494

Contents

Foreword

Hams are a very diverse group. There are so many activities to enjoy that it is difficult for any individual to try each one. New modes and activities seem to be invented almost every month. There is one common element to all these activities—transmitting signals, and receiving them, requires an antenna.

At ARRL Headquarters, we receive more questions about antennas than on any other single subject. Often the questioner is someone new to the hobby, or a more experienced ham who is trying a new band or activity for the first time. Many hams find antennas easy and fun to build and test. This leads to still more questions.

Your Ham Antenna Companion was written to take some of the mystery out of antennas. Paul Danzer, N1II, guides you through the subject as though there was an experienced friend standing by to answer your questions. If you have never built an antenna before, try one of the designs in this book; some take just a few minutes to build. You, too, will be able to join the thousands of hams who say with pride, "The antenna here is homebrewed."

Please let us know how you like this book—drop us a note or use the handy form at the back. Your comments and suggestions are important to us.

David Sumner, K1ZZ
Executive Vice President
August 1995

Preface

As a teenager, I lived in a house with a flat roof. To the best of my knowledge there is still a box of rocks on the roof, much to the mystification of the current owners. My first antenna was a dipole for 20 meters, supported by sections of TV mast at the front and back of the house. In order to bring the feed line down at right angles to the dipole, I placed a wooden box on the center of the roof. The box was in danger of being blown away, so I laboriously filled it by carrying rocks up to the roof. Just where so many rocks came from in the midst of New York City is another story.

Later I owned a home in a suburban area of New Jersey. Fresh out of the Army and armed with tree and telephone pole climbing skills (courtesy of the US Army Signal Corps), I mounted several clothesline pulleys in the trees to hold the ends of a number of antennas. I recently went by my former home and noticed that the pulley in the front tree was still in place.

My current home is surrounded by trees. Invisible to the naked eye, but well known to local birds, squirrels and myself, are a number of lengths of monofilament fishing line dangling from the trees. At the end of each length of monofilament are 3 or 4-ounce fishing sinkers. These are the remnants of unsuccessful attempts to place a line over a tree as an antenna support. I occasionally wonder what thoughts will go through the head of later owners of this property, when they take a tree down or it falls in a storm and they find these pieces of fishing tackle.

From my own experience it is not surprising that antennas and their use provides more discussion, more misinformation and more controversy than any other ham topic. It also drives hams to do the screwiest things. Why else would normally sedate individuals go climbing trees, towers and roofs in the middle of snow storms, heavy rain and temperature extremes just because "something fell down"?

To really understand antennas and their implications requires at least college level and probably graduate school mathematics. To erect and use antennas successfully requires only a little common sense.

This book was written as a companion—a guide—for the ham, new or old, who needs help with antennas. It should supply some of the common sense needed to successfully build and use antennas to get your signal out of the shack or car and into the air. And that's what ham radio is all about.

Acknowledgments

Although only my name appears on the cover, there were other contributors. In fact, there were two groups of them. One group consists of those I can name directly—Peter Budnik, KB1HY; Steve Ford, WB8IMY; Joel Kleinman, N1BKE; Roy Lewallen, W7EL; and R. Dean Straw, N6BV. I am grateful for their suggestions and corrections.

The second group, whom I cannot name individually, are those hams who have chosen over the years to share their antenna ideas with the rest of us. They tried new designs, tested them and then took the time to describe them in writing, so the rest of us could learn from their experience. I hope some of the readers of this book will follow the same path, so we can publish their new antenna ideas and results in *QST*, *The ARRL Handbook for Radio Amateurs* or *The ARRL Antenna Book*.

Paul Danzer, N1II
Assistant Technical Editor, ARRL

CHAPTER 1

Your Rig's Window on the World

What Do You Think Of . . .?

I f you say the word *antenna* it will mean something different to every ham. To me, when I am out for my daily walk with my dog, I would immediately think of the rubber duck antenna on my hand-held 2-meter rig—like the one in the photo of the Kenwood hand-held. Say the same word to Dean Straw, N6BV, and he would imagine you were talking about one of the antennas on his tower. The top antenna is 130 feet from the ground, and that does not include its mountain-top location.

Del Schier, KD1DU, is active on the VHF, UHF and microwave frequencies. Say "antenna" to him and he thinks of a tower such as the Rohn unit in the photo, with a microwave dish perched on top. The gang who ran the Field Day satellite station for the Motor City Radio Club, W8MRM, would think of the automatic computer tracking system that drove their antennas. These antennas were only 6 or 7 feet from the ground—which was all they needed to

Clockwise
from top
left:
-courtesy of
 Kenwood
-courtesy of
 N6BV
-courtesy of
 Rohn tower
-courtesy of
 WA1WLA
-courtesy of
 W8MRM

have their signals reach the satellites.

Constantine Thomas, WA1WLA, would not talk about his antennas—he had six for the HF bands—until he showed you his remotely controlled switch box. Constantine had only one feed line for all the antennas. This switch lets him use one very low-loss feed line. He controls the remote switch box with a rotary switch in his shack.

An antenna installation includes many things: the antenna elements themselves—the parts that radiate your signal—as well as the antenna supports, towers, poles, feed lines or transmission lines, switches, tuning units, baluns and more. A great antenna lying on the ground does not do you much good. Neither does the same antenna 70 feet in the air if it's connected to your rig with lossy transmission line.

In this book you will find information and help on all the parts that make a good antenna system. Whether you are interested in motorcycle mobile or you live in a condominium that does not allow antennas (see Chapter 4), you are not the first ham to ask your question or have that particular problem. We hope you will find the answer here, or perhaps see what other hams have done in the same situation.

Where Does Your Signal go When It Leaves your Antenna?

I use a hand-held rig when I talk to friends on the local repeater. The keyboard buttons on the rig are very small, and my fingers relatively large. Quite often I hit the wrong button, or worse, two buttons at once, and my rig follows an internal program into never-never land. You could say my fingers are not *matched* to the buttons on the rig.

For best performance, all ham stations need several things matched. A *transmission line* connects the rig to the antenna.

The rig must be matched to the transmission line. The other end of the transmission line must be matched to the antenna. Finally, the antenna must be matched to *space*, because that is where the radio-frequency energy goes when it leaves the antenna. Make it tough for the energy to leave the antenna, and the antenna will work poorly. Make it easy—build the antenna from the proper materials and assemble it to the right dimensions—and it will work well. There is a lot more to it, but the basic idea is to get as much power up to the antenna as possible, and then let the energy leave the antenna. Only energy that leaves the antenna—*propagates into space*—does you any good at the receiving end.

Straight Out at VHF and UHF

Put your hand in front of a flashlight and it will cast a shadow. Light is energy at an extremely high frequency—much higher than any of the ham bands. This energy propagates or travels in a straight line or *line of sight*—straight out from the source. Two hams operating on 2 meters from their cars and separated by a hill (Fig 1-1) cannot hear each other. They are not within line of sight. Now place a repeater on a high hill. Everyone in the area can hear the repeater, and therefore the two mobiles who could not talk before now can communicate. This is why repeaters are so popular.

The VHF (very high frequency), UHF (ultra high frequency) and microwave ham bands are at frequencies where the RF energy normally propagates by line of sight. Occasionally the energy will bounce off a weather front or some other object in the sky, but most propagation is directly from one point to another.

You have your choice of types of antennas for these frequencies. *Omnidirectional* antennas, such as a whip antenna on a car or a rubber duck on a hand-held rig, radiate

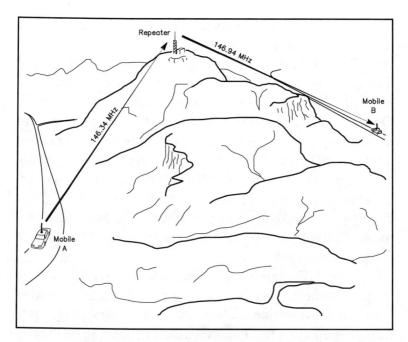

Fig 1-1—A repeater on a high hill or building lets stations talk over any blockage of their line of sight.

and receive in all directions. North, south, east or west—it doesn't matter, because you can be at any direction from a repeater or another station, and you still want to be able to work that station. The idea of turning the car around on an interstate highway, to better hear another station on the 440-MHz band, has very limited appeal!

The other antenna choice is a *directional* antenna. Yagis (beams), quads, quagis, dishes and many others radiate and receive in one favored direction. The idea here is to concentrate as much energy in one direction as possible.

How about HF?

RF energy leaving an HF antenna normally goes

straight out, just as it does at VHF. Then it may bounce around a few times before returning to Earth. It really does that! Basically, RF leaves an HF antenna, travels upward and hits an *ionized layer* of the atmosphere (the *ionosphere*). Some of it then bends back to Earth. Occasionally, the energy will hit one layer, start down, hit another layer, effectively bounce back up, and then bounce a few times before conditions are just right for it to finally bounce back to the Earth's surface. It does not happen in the exact same way, on all parts of the Earth and on all HF (high frequency) bands at the same time, but hams use this mode—called *skip* or *skywave propagation*—to talk to stations all over the world.

Some HF energy leaves the antenna and follows the Earth's surface. This is *ground wave* propagation, and is good for conversations between stations separated by a few miles to perhaps a few hundred miles, depending on the frequency used, time of day or night, and several other factors. Most contacts on HF, other than the local contacts made on ground wave, take advantage of skywave propagation.

Propagation Charts Predict Where the Energy Goes!

To a large extent, where you can reach and how well you and the station on the other side of the world can hear one another is predictable. Each month *QST*, published by the ARRL (see the Resources Guide), has a set of prediction charts. These charts are based on statistics and probability—mathematical tools that tell you what to expect. You do not have to understand the mathematics to use these charts.

The three curves (Fig 1-2) tell you the story. Each month 30 charts are published, showing what to expect from one part of the world to another. The bottom of every chart is the time in UTC (see the Resources Guide for conversion of UTC to your local time).

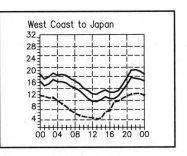

Fig 1-2—This propagation chart predicts that a West Coast US station at 0800 UTC can work Japan on the 14-MHz band on 50% of the days. The lowest frequency that can be used (dashed line) is 7 MHz, and on 10% of the days (upper solid line) the upper limit is about 17 MHz. Therefore, according to this prediction, 20 meters is the best and perhaps only choice.

Pick the chart that covers your location and the place you want to work. Select the time on the bottom axis, and then run your finger straight up. The top solid curve tells you the **highest** frequency that will allow you to talk to the other location (at the time you picked)—not every day but on 10% of the days. Therefore, on 3 days each month, the ham band at a frequency just below this curve will be your best bet. Usually, the highest frequency you can use will have the strongest signals. This is one reason to try to use the highest possible ham band.

Want to be a bit more conservative? Use the second solid curve. This one is for 50% of the days in a month. Pick the ham band just below this curve, and on 15 days of the month you should be able to make contact.

The lower limit is given by the dashed line curve. To be successful, you must use a ham band above this dashed line. Just remember, these charts as based on statistics. It means if you try it often enough, the prediction will be true. Unfortunately, it is not necessarily true on the exact date you want to show a friend how easily you can talk to some far-off station!

Low Elevation Angles—What's The Fuss?

Before we leave propagation, take a look at the two drawings in Fig 1-3. In (A) some RF energy leaves the ground at a high angle—say 20° from the horizontal—bounces off an ionized layer, and comes back to Earth. In (B) the energy leaves at a much lower angle—perhaps 2 or 3° from the horizontal. The distance covered in one bounce or *hop* is much greater. This drawing is not the complete picture. But it does illustrate why you will hear so much about having *low-angle* radiation from your HF antenna. The lower the angle of radiation for most of the energy, the longer the hop. The longer the hop, the farther you can usually work. The exact mechanism of the bouncing around in the layers is vastly more complicated. The Resources Guide has places to look for additional information.

dB and SWR—Nothing to Get Excited About

You probably have read in one or two books, or seen in advertisements, numbers followed by *dB*, the abbreviation for *decibels*. We often measure the gain (amplification) or loss (attenuation) of a signal in an amplifier, antenna, feed line or other electronic device in terms of dB.

Hams also have traditionally used *S-units* to tell how strong a signal is at the receiving end of a contact. "You are S8 here, OM." There is, of course, a relationship between gaining or losing a few dB and going up or down an S-unit at the far end. But before you get too excited about a few dB, read Chapter 5. A gain or loss of a few dB can be significant, but perhaps not always as significant as you think.

The same holds true for measurements of *SWR*—standing wave ratio. The units used are, as the name suggests, a ratio. *Two to one* is usually written as 2:1, and

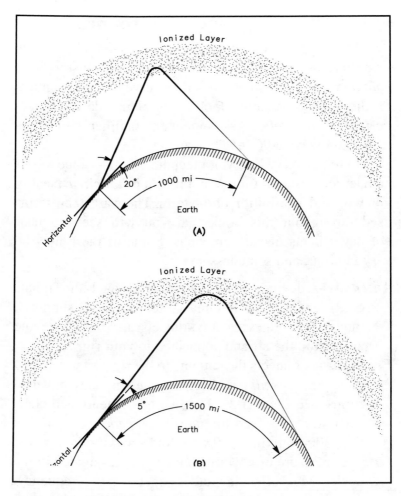

Fig 1-3—As the elevation angle of the RF energy leaving your antenna decreases, the length of the hop increases.

again many hams believe disaster approaches if the SWR they measure is above some magic value, such as 1.5:1. SWR is interesting, and important, but once more, before you get too excited, read Chapter 5 and see when to worry and when not to worry.

The Language of Antennas

Every group, every profession, every hobby has its own jargon. Sometimes the words are historical—*counterpoise*—and sometimes they serve to give members of the group a technical or professional description—*peripheral arterioles*. Ask someone unfamiliar with tennis if they know what "6-love" means!

In this book, whenever a technical term—some of our ham jargon—is used for the first time it is *italicized*. Nearby you will find a definition of the term. There are a few terms used throughout this book that you will see and hear whenever hams discuss antennas. Some of these may be very familiar, and some less so.

Antenna—A device that picks up or sends out radio signals or RF energy. An antenna system includes supports, mounts, feed lines and anything else needed to keep the antenna in the air and connected to your rig.

Feed Line—Connects the antenna to the rig. Often referred to as the *transmission line*. It comes in many physical forms (see Chapter 5). The two most mentioned characteristics of a feed line are the *impedance*—50-ohm line, 300-ohm line, 450-ohm line—and the *losses*.

Loss—A measure of how much energy is dissipated in the device. Most often, the losses depend on the frequency. A section of feed line not designed for VHF can have 5 or 10 times as much loss on the 2-meter band as it has on the 80-meter band.

Antenna Tuners—Also called *Transmatches*, tuners connect a feed line to a rig, or a feed line to an antenna, with minimum loss in the entire system. They usually consist of a network of 2 or 3 variable inductors and capacitors.

Gain—Fig 1-4 is a drawing of an antenna, as seen from the

top. You are looking straight down on a single element antenna. Imagine it is a whip antenna of a certain length, mounted on the ground, with its tip pointed to the sky. The circle, lightly shaded, shows that the power radiated from the whip antenna is equal in all directions. This antenna is called *omnidirectional*.

In (B) we have changed the whip antenna into some other kind of antenna. This one radiates the same total power—from the same transmitter— in a half circle. The darker shading shows all the power, which used to go in a full circle, is now constrained to a half circle. Therefore, anywhere in the half circle, the strength of the signal you would receive is twice the strength you would receive anywhere in the full circle in (A). We have the same total power going into the antenna. The antenna is radiating this power over half the area it did before. Therefore a signal in this area must be twice as strong as before.

Finally the definition. We say the antenna in (B)

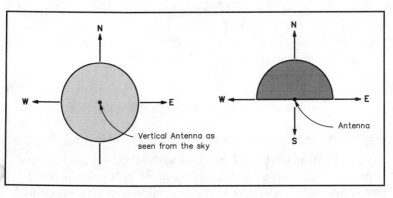

Fig 1-4—If you take the energy from one area and concentrate it into another, the signal strength will increase in the second area. The same total energy from the area in A is concentrated into half the area in B. The antenna in B has a gain of 2 (3 dB) as compared to the antenna in A.

has a gain of 2 as compared to the antenna in (A), since it puts out a signal twice a strong as the antenna in (A).

Gain in an antenna does not amplify your transmitter power. It simply takes power from the directions you are not interested in, and radiates it into a direction you are interested in! Thus, your signal is stronger in the favored direction.

Patterns or beam shapes—The shaded areas in Fig 1-4 are the patterns of these two antennas. Fig 1-5 is a pattern of a high gain antenna. It shows most of the energy has

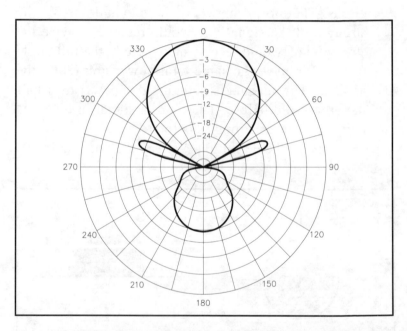

Fig 1-5—This is a typical *horizontal* pattern for a Yagi antenna. It pictures the antenna as though you were in the sky, looking down. Around the circle is azimuth, or direction along the Earth. The front of the antenna points to 0° or north. The farther the heavy line is from the center of the circle, the more energy comes out of the antenna in that direction. The highest gain is called the peak of the beam, at 0°. At 90° there is almost no energy coming from the antenna.

been concentrated into a single *beam*. There is some energy coming out from the back and sides. These small beams, or *lobes*, are called *backlobes* and *sidelobes*.

Fig 1-5 is in the *horizontal plane*; that is, as though you were standing in the sky above the antenna and looking directly down. Fig 1-6 is a pattern in the *vertical plane*—as through you were standing on the Earth and looking at the antenna. In this case the antenna is a simple whip having a very wide vertical beam.

Polarization—A vertical antenna, such as a single piece or wire mounted on the ground, and poking toward the sky, radiates energy that we say is *vertically polarized*. Take the same antenna and mount it parallel to the Earth, and we say it is *horizontally polarized*. Normally, at VHF, UHF and microwave frequencies, two stations talking will use the same polarization. At HF the polarization is not usually important, except at very short ranges.

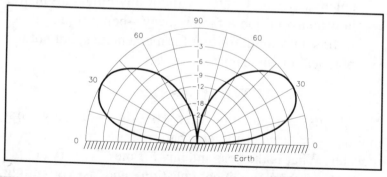

Fig 1-6—This is a typical *vertical* plane antenna pattern. It is drawn as though you were standing on the ground, looking at the side of the antenna. The highest gain (peak of the beam) is at 30°, with almost no energy at 90° (straight up). For most antennas—line of sight in VHF and UHF, or to work DX on HF—you would like the peak of the beam (highest gain) to be closer to 0°. Then most RF energy would go out parallel to the Earth's surface.

RF burns—This really is not a definition. It is an explanation of a term you will hear from people who have been unfortunate enough to have received an RF burn. When you touch an antenna, exposed feed line or some other device carrying more than a few watts of RF power, your hand will draw an arc. This not the same as receiving a shock from a voltage source. In the very lightest form, the RF energy burns a little, deep hole—very painful—in your finger. It is an experience most hams agree they can do without!

SWR or standing wave ratio—A measure of the match between your rig and the feed line or the feed line and the antenna. Chapter 5 discusses the practical effects of SWR on your signal.

Space and *free space*—When power leaves your antenna, we say it is radiated into space. In the early days of radio, the term *ether* was used to describe the "fluid" that conducted the radio waves. Free space has a special definition. It refers to a theoretical area where an antenna can be located without anything—no matter how many millions of miles away—being able to affect it. It is a useful definition for mathematics, but not too practical in any ham's universe.

What Next?

"I just bought my first HF rig"—or "my first mobile"—or "I want to get a better signal from the local repeater. What is the best antenna for me?" A very simple question, a very common question, and as you might imagine, a question without a direct answer. There is no "best antenna."

Almost anything will work as an antenna—some things well and some not so well. If you are a new ham, or just new to a band or mode, one approach is to build a low-cost version of the antenna you are considering. Try it, and then decide if a permanent version is for you. Having trouble accessing the local packet node and considering a 12-element Yagi? Build a 2 or 3-element Yagi and see if it helps. Then you might decide to buy a commercial unit, or you might decide to try another approach.

Want to work more DX on the 40-meter band? Before you spend a great deal of money and effort on a 70-foot tower, try a full wave loop. It may help from your location or it may not.

There are many software packages available today that let you design and optimize an antenna. Many of them are simple to use and a great deal of fun. You can easily spend hours, days, and weeks tweaking

Fig 1-7—Worried about how to work on an antenna atop a high tower? U.S. Tower makes this motor-driven unit to crank their tower up and down. Up to operate, and down to inspect the antenna and repair it if necessary. This also comes in very handy when the weather forecast is an approaching hurricane!

your own design—a thing of great beauty and personal pride—until you have squeezed every last drop of performance from it.

Go ahead. Enjoy the experience of designing your own. But when you finally build it and put it into place, don't forget some of the practical things covered in this book. The

Fig 1-8—One of the best parts of antenna work to Lee Aurick, W1SE, is putting them up. Here at a Field Day site he uses a sling shot and spinning reel to toss a sinker over a tree. The fishing line is connected to a light rope, which in turn is used to pull one end of a wire antenna to treetop height.

height is very important. Don't design an antenna for mounting at 150 feet, when you are going to support it on a 30-foot pole. If you live on a granite mountain in Vermont or over a non-conductive site in the desert, don't assume perfect ground. Finally, don't bother to optimize the performance when you are going to use questionable feed line, snatched up at 10 cents per foot at a flea market.

All simulation and design programs have limits. Understand the valid range of values for the program. Build your antenna as you have simulated it, and mount it as you have simulated it. Only then will you get the performance the program promises.

This book was written to give you some guidance on antennas, and the various problems you can encounter when you are working with antennas. Need to pick a feed line? See Chapter 5. Worried about safety? Chapter 7. Whatever your problem, someone probably has had the same problem before. The nice thing about antennas is they are rarely a lifetime commitment. Build it or buy it, try it, and in a few years you are probably going to want to change it! That is the nature of ham radio antennas.

CHAPTER 2

At VHF and UHF It's Mostly Line of Sight

T he most popular operating modes today are on the VHF and UHF bands. Perhaps more hams are using FM repeaters and packet radio than all other modes combined. Most of this operation is on the 2-meter (146 MHz) and 70-cm (440 MHz) bands, with a lesser amount on 222 MHz. Some hams work DX—called *weak signal* work—but most hams use these bands for local communications. Therefore, you need just enough antenna to get the job done. There is no advantage in using an expensive high gain antenna to bring up the local repeater or packet node 10 miles away when a smaller and cheaper antenna will do the job just as well. The smaller and simpler the antenna, the more likely it will stay up during wind and ice storms, and the less likely you will be heard and perhaps cause interference on another repeater some distance away.

If you are like most hams who stick with local QSOs on VHF or UHF, the job of picking, building or buying and erecting an antenna is pretty straightforward. If your main interest is weak signal work, satellite operation or winning every VHF contest, however, you will also want to check the Resources Guide at the back of this book for additional information.

This chapter is going to walk you through VHF and UHF antennas, both homebrewed and commercial. Even if you don't want to try your hand at building your own antenna—which may only take a few minutes and less than $10 on VHF/UHF— the construction details will help you pick out and buy the antenna you really want. As you know, judging an antenna (or a car or anything else) by a fancy model name may not make for a very good purchase.

We are going to cover antennas for use from your home or apartment (fixed location). We will also discuss mobile antennas as well as antennas for hand-held transceivers.

Fig 2-1—This portable VHF antenna comes with a view. It was used for a contest by the San Francisco ARC.

Home Sweet Home, or What Will the Neighbors Say?

"Location, location, location." That's what real estate people will tell you are the three most important things to consider before buying a home. You could say something similar about picking an antenna for use at home. Since the primary path for VHF/UHF signals is *line of sight*, the higher the antenna the longer (or better) the line of sight. Even if you are within 5 or so miles of the local repeater, a hill or building in the path can block your signal. It is not uncommon for a ham living in a hilly area to be able to reach another station with a hand-held transceiver and *rubber duck* antenna on the second floor of a house. However, on the first floor of the same house, the equipment will either work only in a few spots or require a better antenna.

Suppose you are having a hard time making a solid contact with another station. One choice is a small, lightweight (2 or 3 pound) ground-plane antenna atop a 25-foot guyed TV mast. The other choice may be a 15-element Yagi with a rotator (total weight 20 to 25 pounds) on a 5-foot rooftop mount. You may be much better off choosing the smaller but higher antenna. Remember: VHF and UHF waves travel as light waves do—in a straight line called the *line of sight*. If your problem is a hill or building interrupting the line of sight, more antenna height rather than a more complex antenna is usually the better solution.

FM as used today requires vertically polarized antennas (see Chapter 1). If you have or plan to get a multimode transceiver and operate CW or SSB, you will also need a horizontally polarized antenna.

Picking an Antenna

The fun part of picking an antenna for these frequencies is that you can actually build one rather quickly and try it out. Your construction does not have to be perfect nor must you build it hurricane proof. Then, after trying your creation (if you like it) you might either buy a similar more rugged commercial unit, or build one that will withstand the weather for many years.

Vertical Antennas

Certainly the most popular antennas for packet and

FM/repeater operation are single-element vertical antennas. Single element means they have one radiating element rather than several, one behind the other, as does a beam or Yagi. Vertical, as we said in Chapter 1, means the radiating element is vertical to the Earth's surface instead of running parallel to the Earth's surface. As you might expect, it does not have to be rotated or pointed to the other station. Thus,

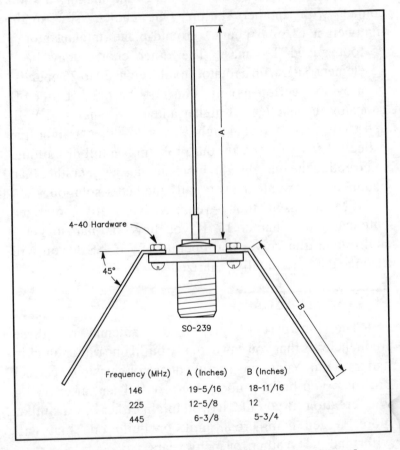

Frequency (MHz)	A (Inches)	B (Inches)
146	19-5/16	18-11/16
225	12-5/8	12
445	6-3/8	5-3/4

Fig 2-2—Simple ground-plane antenna for the 146, 222 and 440-MHz bands. The vertical element and the radials are lengths of $^3/_{32}$ or $^1/_{16}$ brass rod. If you prefer, build it with #10 or #12 solid copper wire.

verticals are equally effective in all directions, or *omnidirectional*.

Vertical antennas can be designed to be anywhere from a few inches to 20 or more feet in length (height). Best of all, you can make one for a few dollars and get a feel for what it takes to build your own antenna.

At the cost of one coaxial connector socket, some hardware and a few feet of wire, the ground-plane antenna in Fig 2-2 can be yours in just a few minutes. For quick construction you can strip the insulation from a piece of 10 or 12 gauge solid copper wire and use it for this project. *Romex* or *BX* cable such as that sold for house wiring contains this type of wire.

Mount the antenna temporarily by soldering a mating plug (PL-259) to the coax feed line and connect it to the socket (SO-239). Tape the coax to the top of a mast or pole so the SO-239 and top vertical element are just above the pole. For more permanent mounting you can make a homemade L-bracket (Fig 2-3) and clamp the vertical part of the bracket to a length of TV mast with standard TV U-bolts.

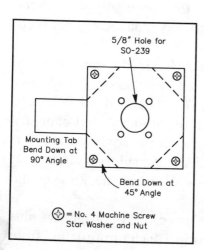

5/8" Hole for
SO-239

Mounting Tab
Bend Down at
90° Angle

Bend Down at
45° Angle

= No. 4 Machine Screw
Star Washer and Nut

Fig 2-3—The plate should be just big enough to mount the SO-239 connector. After drilling the holes, bend the tab down and clamp it to the mast.

Finally, connect the other end of the coax feed line to your rig. Congratulations—you have just built a perfectly good antenna. Like the way it performs? Maybe you will want to build it up a little stronger and more weather resistant.

Fig 2-4—MFJ manufactures this ground plane. It can be used on 146 MHz right out of the box, or the elements can be cut for use on 222 or 440 MHz. *(photo courtesy of MFJ)*

You can buy the commercial ground plane in Fig 2-4 from several amateur supply distributors. After all, building is not everyone's cup of tea. But whether you build or buy a new antenna, use a good quality feed line (see Chapter 5).

Other commercial vertical antennas are shown in Figs 2-5 and 2-6. Notice some of them are longer than the radiating element on a simple ground plane. By making them longer they are really just several radiating elements *stacked* vertically (connected end to end) to get more gain.

Jim Reynante, KD6GLF, described another vertical antenna you can build for just a few dollars (actually a few cents) in September 1994 *QST*. It's called a J-Pole, and consists of a single length of ordinary 300-ohm TV twinlead. Construction of the antenna requires just a few steps with a sharp knife, a ruler and a soldering iron. Best of all, it is a *dual bander*; it works on both the 2-meter and 70-cm (440 MHz) bands.

First cut a length of twinlead exactly 55¹/₈ inches plus 1 inch or 56¹/₈ inches long. Strip 1 inch of insulation from one end, twist the two bare wires together as shown in Fig 2-7, and solder. You now have a 55¹/₈-inch "U" shaped conductor.

Next notch out a section of wire with its surrounding

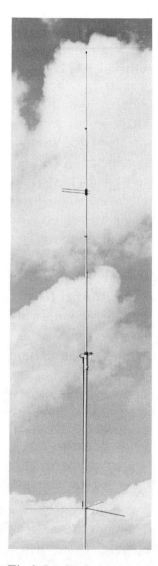

Fig 2-5—Cushcraft's Ringo Ranger series of vertical antennas are very popular for both FM-repeater and packet work. *(photo courtesy of Cushcraft)*

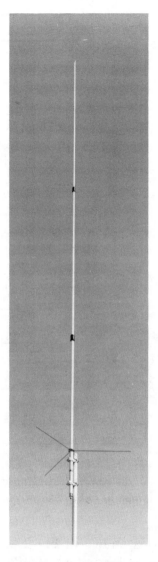

Fig 2-6—Comet makes this dual-band (146 and 440-MHz) vertical antenna. It is almost 18 feet high. *(photo courtesy of Comet/ NCG)*

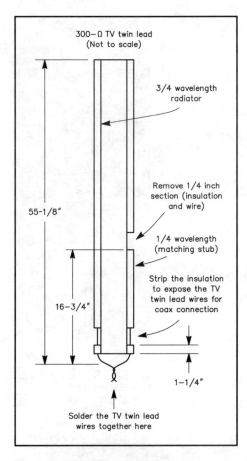

300-Ω TV twin lead
(Not to scale)

3/4 wavelength
radiator

Remove 1/4 inch
section (insulation
and wire)

55-1/8"

1/4 wavelength
(matching stub)

Strip the insulation
to expose the TV
twin lead wires for
coax connection

16-3/4"

1-1/4"

Solder the TV twin lead
wires together here

Fig 2-7—The basic J-pole layout. The areas where the insulation or wires must be cut are shown (see text).

insulation 16³/₄ inches up from the bottom (as shown in the illustration on the right side). Now the "J" shaped conductor—the long (55¹/₈-inch) conductor—is on the left and the short (16³/₄-inch) conductor is on the right. The bottom of the "J" is the piece you soldered in the first step.

Complete the cutting operation by removing a short section of insulation 1¹/₄ inches from the bottom on both sides. You don't have to remove very much insulation, since you just have to be able to solder to the wires.

Finally, solder a length of RG-58 coax as shown in Fig 2-8. The antenna operates best when a device called a *balun* is used. Baluns are discussed in Chapter 5. For this antenna, the balun consists of several small pieces of ferrite material placed around the coax. The ferrite is a mixture of metal oxides and glue—in this case called #43 material. The Resources Guide section in the back of this book has further details on the balun.

Tape the antenna to a wooden pole or hold it up by a length of monofilament fishing line from an overhanging tree branch. For a weatherproof installation, put the antenna in a length of plastic hose and seal the ends. Stick with a transparent hose—most plastics that are transparent to visible light are also transparent to radio frequency energy. Don't be surprised if the SWR changes a little when the antenna is placed in a plastic enclosure.

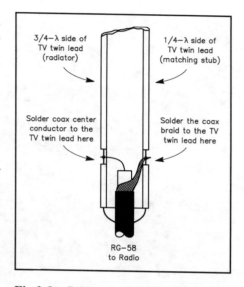

Fig 2-8—Solder the RG-58 coax feed line directly to the antenna. The center conductor of the coax connects to the longer side of the J-pole and the coax braid to the shorter side.

Yagis and Quads

If you live a good distance from a repeater or need more "punch" to make a connection with the nearest packet node, an antenna with a higher gain than a simple ground plane may be the solution. *Yagis*, or *beams* as they are often called, are generally more complicated to put up than simple verticals but do offer higher gain. *Quads*, which are Yagis with loop-shaped elements, have generally the same advantages and disadvantages as Yagis.

Figs 2-9, 2-10 and 2-11 show a few of the many available commercial Yagis. For repeater, packet and other FM communications, the Yagis are mounted so they are verti-

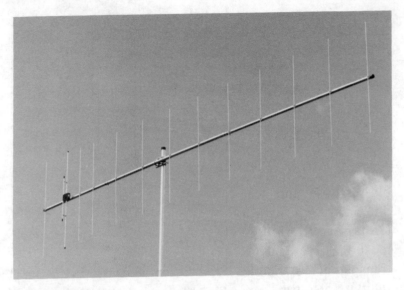

Fig 2-9—This Cushcraft vertically polarized Yagi is mounted to a mast in the center of the boom. *(photo courtesy of Cushcraft)*

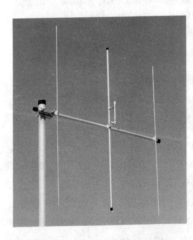

Fig 2-10—A slightly smaller (4-element) Cushcraft Yagi mounts with the mast at the end of the boom out of the field of the elements. *(photo courtesy of Cushcraft)*

cally polarized—that is, the elements run up and down. Yagis are designed very carefully. The lengths of the elements, spacing between elements and diameter of the elements all affect the performance. Often without thinking, a ham will mount the Yagi as shown in Fig 2-9 with a metal mast in the middle of the elements. This can reduce the performance of the Yagi considerably.

Fortunately, some commercial Yagi manufacturers

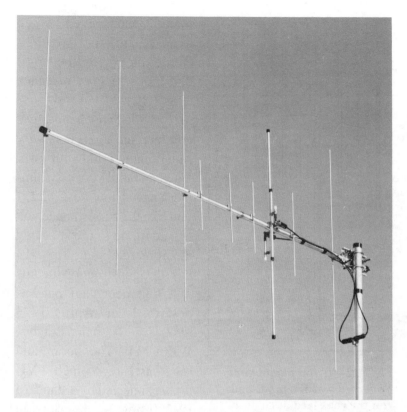

Fig 2-11—A vertically polarized Cushcraft antenna. Designed for vertical polarization, the mast is behind the antenna. This dual-band model A270-10S provides operation on both 144 and 440 MHz. *(photo courtesy of Cushcraft)*

have products designed to accommodate vertical mounting on a metal mast. The Cushcraft dual-band Yagi in Fig 2-11 is one of these. Ask about the mounting before you buy.

There are several solutions to this problem. One is to mount the Yagi at the end of its boom, as shown in Fig 2-10. The metal mast is behind the last Yagi element and does not affect performance very much. Another approach is to use a few feet of wooden mast. A 1½ or 2-inch wooden pole, soaked in wood preservative, will have a useful life of

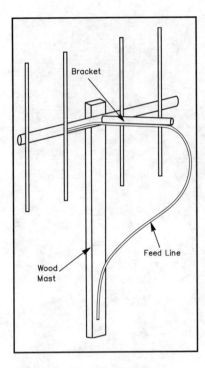

Fig 2-12—If you mount your Yagi on a wooden mast, and run the coax feed at right angles to the elements, you will be able to keep the feed line out of the pattern.

many years even when exposed to the weather. Route the feed line so it does not affect performance (Fig 2-12).

While many hams buy a commercial Yagi, it is very satisfying to build your own. You can build your own simple Yagi at low cost, and if you like the performance you can continue to use it or buy a commercial unit. Fig 2-13 has the construction details of a 3-element Yagi that was described in April 1993 *QST* by Nathan Loucks, WB0CMT. The boom and the mast are ³/₄-inch PVC pipe, connected by a standard PVC fitting. As described in *QST,* brass screws were used to fasten the pipe to the fitting, but you can also use glue designed for PVC pipe.

The elements are made of ¹/₁₆-inch brass brazing or hobby rods. Drill holes that provide a snug fit for the elements and epoxy them in place. Notice the center or "driven" element is not continuous; it consists of two halves. Solder the RG-8 coax feed line to the element halves close to the boom as shown in Fig 2-14.

After building the Yagi, adjust the length of the center element by loosening the wire clamps and sliding the end pieces up or down (for best SWR). You can also

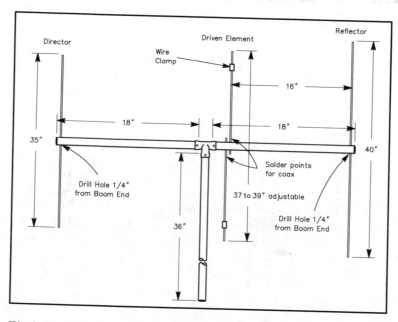

Fig 2-13—Construction details of a 3-element Yagi for 2 meters. Radiation of a Yagi is in the direction from the reflector toward the driven element and the director.

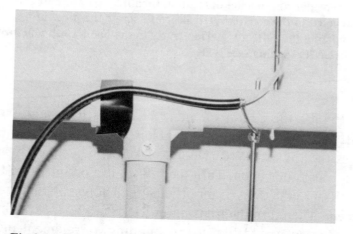

Fig 2-14—The coax cable feed line is soldered to the two halves of the driven element.

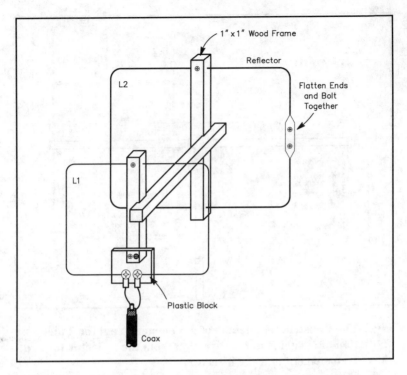

Fig 2-15—A few pieces of wood and a few feet of aluminum wire produce a 2-element quad. As shown it is horizontally polarized. For repeater and packet operation, turn it 90° so the side connected to the coax is vertical. Don't screw the piece of wood supporting the reflector permanently to the boom until you have adjusted its spacing (see text).

just make the center element 39 inches long and carefully cut off ⅛ inch at a time from each end till you just pass the lowest SWR. Do not make the adjustment when the transmitter is on. Turn the transmitter on, measure the SWR, turn the transmitter off, and then adjust or cut the element. Then turn the transmitter back on.

If you would like to try building a 2-element quad antenna using simple wood construction, take a look at

Fig 2-15. Three pieces of 1×1-inch wood are used for the boom and to hold the loops. The reflector is made from a piece of #8 aluminum wire. Cut the wire for the reflector 87 inches long plus 1 extra inch for the overlap shown. The ends of the wire are flattened and held together by a screw through the flattened areas. If you like you can skip this step and just hold the ends together with a small U-bolt such as those used to fasten guy wires.

Bend the reflector wire into a square with each side 21³/₄ inches long (plus the extra inch on one end—so the last side is 22³/₄ inches long). The driven element is a piece of wire 83 inches long. Cut the wire 84 inches long. Each side of this element is 20³/₄ inches long with a slight overlap at the bottom. Wrap this extra half inch on each end of the bottom around the screws shown on the little plastic block.

Assemble the antenna as shown in the figure. The 50-ohm feed line is connected to the driven element by wrapping its conductors around the screws.

Changing the distance between the two loops is the only adjustment needed. Start at 9 inches, and slide the piece of wood holding the reflector back and forth for minimum SWR. Don't expect to achieve a 1:1 SWR. Many SWR meters are not accurate at these frequencies, and unless you have a very long feed line or very lossy line you will not see any substantial extra loss from SWRs up to 2:1 or so.

Hand-Held Units

Hand-held transceivers, or *handi-talkies* as they are sometimes known, usually come with a shortened antenna called a *rubber duck* (Fig 2-16). The penalty for a short antenna such as this is lower gain. Usually the longer the rubber duck antenna the higher the gain, until the antenna reaches the size of a full ¹/₄-wavelength antenna. You can also buy a commercial ¹/₄-wavelength antenna that is col-

Fig 2-16—Most hand-helds, such as this ICOM, come with a *rubber duck* antenna. These compact antennas can be from 2 to 12 inches long for 2 meters. *(photo courtesy of ICOM)*

lapsible. Some must be extended to their full length (about 19 inches for 2 meters) before transmitting and others will work as well as a rubber duck when collapsed.

If you want to roll your own $1/4$-wavelength antenna you can do so by using a BNC connector with a length of *piano wire* soldered to the center pin. This wire is available at many hobby stores in 24 and 36-inch lengths.

After assembling the BNC connector, fill the area between the wire and the connector shell with silastic, RTV or hot melt glue. Cut the wire to a length of $19^{3}/4$ inches and coil the end of the wire into a little loop to prevent inadvertently stabbing anyone with the wire.

Extended length whips are also available. These are usually made to be *electrically* (not physically) $1/2$-wavelength or $5/8$ wavelength long. They do provide an extra measure of gain but at the cost of applying considerable force to the BNC connector on the end of your hand-held rig. A number of failures of this connector have been reported.

One final accessory you can try is a ground plane for your hand-held. A 19-inch piece of wire attached to the **outside** of the antenna connector will act as a ground plane or the second half of a dipole antenna. Some hams claim an increase in signal strength using either homebrewed (they cut the length of wire themselves) or commercial units; others report no difference at all. Since the cost of a 19-inch piece of wire is small, you might want to try this one yourself.

If you travel a lot for business or vacation consider a better antenna that you can use in your hotel room. The J-pole antenna described earlier in this chapter is a good choice for packing in a suitcase. One commercial roll-up, pack-away unit made by MFJ is shown in Fig 2-17.

You can also build a Yagi that folds up to a 3-inch cube to fit in your suitcase. A 48×48-inch sheet of 1 or 2-mil thick plastic, sold as a painter's drop cloth, forms the base of the antenna. The elements are made from window alarm tape. They should be cut to the dimensions shown in Fig 2-13. To use your packable Yagi, hang it from the corners on the window or wall. When you are finished, fold up the plastic and put it in your suitcase.

VHF Mobile—But Keep Your Eyes on the Road

VHF/UHF and mobile operation just go together.

Fig 2-17—Have antenna will travel. Just roll this MFJ J-pole into a small coil and stick it in your pocket or suitcase. *(photo courtesy of MFJ)*

Fig 2-20—This Comet model GR-5M mobile antenna mount fastens to the edge of a trunk lid. A special low-loss narrow coax cable section is used near the mount to prevent the trunk lid from pinching the cable. *(photo courtesy of Comet/NCG)*

Fig 2-18—An unusual suction cup mount (model WS-1M) is made by Comet for temporary use in any situation. The photograph was taken from the inside of the car and shows the connector for the feed line. You can see the antenna extending vertically on the outside of the glass. Through-the-glass mounts should not be used with glass that is tinted with a metallization process. *(photo courtesy of Comet/NCG)*

HF mobile was and is very popular, but background noise and splatter can make it very annoying for occupants of the car. Channelized VHF/UHF FM eliminates this problem by using a squelch function to remove background noise when no one is talking, and the agreed-to channel spacing just about eliminates interference from nearby QSOs. It is no wonder then that there are a whole host of antennas available for mobile operation.

Figs 2-18, 2-19 and 2-20 show some of these. If you don't mind drilling a hole in the top of your car, a simple

Fig 2-19—These three mag-mount antennas belong to Jeff Bauer, WA1MBK. Having a separate antenna for 144, 222 and 440 MHz allows him to work three bands at once!

¼-wavelength whip does a nice job, with the added advantage of reducing RF that might be radiated into the passenger compartment. This hole is usually drilled above the interior dome light and the connecting feed line is fed from that point under the headliner down inside the door pillar.

In addition to ¼-wavelength antennas, ⅝-wavelength antennas are also popular. These units will have slightly more gain than the smaller ¼-wavelength antenna, when mounted in the center of a large flat expanse of metal such as a car rooftop. If mounted on a trunk lid they do give slightly more gain but only in some directions, depending on the shielding and reflections from the rest of the car body.

Mounting options, assuming you are not going to drill a hole in your new car, range from through-the-glass to magnetic mounts to trunk-lid clips. Through-the-glass types may not be as efficient as other antennas, but they are convenient to use on some cars. They cannot be used on tinted windows where the tinting is done with a metallized layer in the glass. Magnetic mounts are pretty reliable but require the feed line to enter the car through a window or door. Trunk-lid mounts are easy to install; the feed line runs from inside the trunk into the passenger compartment.

Through-the-glass antennas have most of their radiating element above the metal roof. Roof-mounted antennas have all of the radiating element above the roof. In both cases the metal roof provides protective shielding from RF fields at the power (10 to 50 watts) often found in mobile ham rigs. Trunk-lid mounts allow a considerable portion of the radiating element to radiate an RF field directly into the passenger compartment. This could cause problems. Read Chapter 7 of this book (Safety) before you install a mobile rig that runs more than a few watts.

CHAPTER 3

HF Antennas—
From Around the
Corner to Around
the World

All antennas consist of one or more radiating elements, a transmission line, a few insulators and a connector or two. Okay, that's enough theory. Now let's build an HF antenna!

No, I am not kidding. A little later in this chapter we will talk about the various types of antennas you can erect for the HF bands, how to select one, and how to either build or buy it. But for now, we are going to build a perfectly usable antenna. Then, once we have gotten our feet wet (or fingers bent!), we can back off and look at the whole topic of HF—high frequency—antennas for the 1.8 to 28-MHz bands.

Most hams have *junk boxes*—collections of parts and pieces that are "too good to throw out," or "I may need this in the future." A few hams have *junque boxes*, but their contents are similar and not necessarily better. To build our

HF Antennas   3-1

antenna you will have to look into your junk box, the back of your garage, tool shed or basement for a few parts. If you don't have them, you can go down to your local hardware store, discount store or Radio Shack and pick them up for a few bucks. When we are finished, these parts and a few minutes of your time will become a 10-meter antenna. It won't be a permanent antenna, but it will work, and you will be able to see there is no real mystery in making HF antennas.

Parts

You need about 20 feet of wire. Insulated, bare, solid, stranded—it doesn't make any difference. Pick a size or *gauge* between 14 and 22. The lower the number, the larger the wire diameter. In this case, for a temporary antenna, it won't make much difference.

Your rig will connect to the antenna through a length of coax cable. If you want to try the antenna in the room, at low power, you only need a 10-foot length. For testing outside, you need perhaps 25 feet. That will limit how far from your shack you can mount the antenna, but it will get it outside for a test. Almost any coax will do—numbers starting with RG-8, RG-58, RG-59 or anything else you can get your hands on is fine. For this first antenna, with a very short feed line, the losses in the feed line will not be a problem.

Three insulators—glass, ceramic or even 2-inch long pieces of wood with two holes drilled in them—are needed. You could even use plastic cut from food containers, or rubber bands, but then you might have trouble soldering the antenna together without melting the plastic.

To hold the antenna in place, a length of heavy string or cord will be tied to each end.

Finally, a coax connector, called a *PL-259*, is needed

to fit your coax. Normally, as described in Chapter 5, you should always use a connector that solders onto the coax cable. But for this first antenna—and just for this temporary antenna—you can, if you wish, use a *no-solder push-on* coax connector.

Put it Together

We are going to make a *dipole antenna*. It is one of the most popular "first" antennas for the HF bands. From the name (**di**pole), you can surmise it has two pieces. Often it is called a half-wave dipole or $\lambda/2$ dipole, where λ (the Greek letter *lambda*) stands for wavelength. We picked the 10-meter band for our antenna, because it has the shortest wavelength. Again, from the name of the band, $\lambda=10$ meters. A half wavelength ($\lambda/2$) is therefore 10/2 or 5 meters. Converting meters to feet, a half wavelength is approximately 16 feet.

Later in the chapter we will use a standard formula for calculating the length of an antenna—but for now we know the length of our test antenna should be about 16 feet. Cut a piece of wire 17 feet long, and then cut it in half again (**di**pole = two equal pieces). If your wire is insulated, remove about 4 inches of insulation from each end, and make the assembly as drawn in Fig 3-1A. We cut the wire a little longer than the calculation said we should—the extra length allows us to double the wire over to do the twisting shown in Fig 3-1B.

Next, take one end of the coax and remove about 6 inches of the outer (usually black) plastic covering. Take apart about 6 inches of the braid underneath. In Chapter 5 there is a figure showing a nice way to do this, but for now just take the braid apart. Finally, strip 2 inches of insulation from the remaining center of the coax. Your coax end should now look similar to Fig 3-1C. Then twist the coax

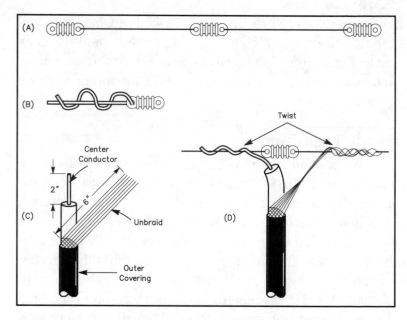

Fig 3-1—You can build this temporary dipole in just a few minutes.

center conductor and braid over the two wires on the center insulator, as shown in Fig 3-1D.

Now we are ready to solder the four wire ends in Fig 3-1A. At this point you might expect a long discussion on soldering. Sorry, but all we want to do here is put up a temporary antenna. Therefore, take a large soldering iron—at least 100 watts—electrical solder with rosin (non-acid) flux inside the solder—and quickly solder the ends. If the wire is old, and perhaps has a little surface oxidation, extra rosin soldering flux (available in tubes from hardware stores or Radio Shack) can help.

The faster you solder the connections, the less likely you are to melt some of the coax insulation. That is why you want to use a large soldering iron. Go in, solder quickly, and remove the soldering iron!

Finally, at the other end of the coax, attach the push-on coax connector. Carefully follow the instructions printed on the connector's packaging.

Now you have it. Instant antenna. With the string or cord attached to the end insulators, you can mount the antenna across a room, or string it between two nearby trees. It is not a permanent antenna—we didn't weatherproof the end of the coax, nor did we cut the antenna length to the precise best value! **But you built it, you put it up, and if you connect the coax fitting to your rig it will really work!** Not bad for a few minutes of work.

From this point on, every other HF antenna we discuss will be a variation of this basic antenna. There will be at least one conductor, called a radiating *element*. Sometimes a second element is replaced by a *ground plane* or just a ground connection. Some antennas will require a specific type of coax or other transmission line to operate correctly, and others will do just fine with any length of a good quality coax. Now you have built one, and when we say "connect the coax to the antenna," you have an idea what this really means.

Picking a New Antenna

I own a small *antenna farm*. If you have never heard the term, it means I have more than one or two antennas around my home. In fact I have five! I am lucky to have that many. Some hams can just manage one, due to their location or for other reasons. There are some hams who are luckier than I am—they can put up 120-foot towers or 1000-foot-long pieces of wire!

Most hams pick the best antenna they can erect, knowing the limits of what their home will allow, or their piggybank can stand. This chapter talks about the most common HF antennas you will want to consider. It gives you the advantages and disadvantages, and points out some of the myths surrounding some of these antennas.

Picking an HF antenna is no different from making any other important decision—you want to get the most for your investment of time and money. For example, if you are going to operate on most of the HF bands, and want to work both DX and local stations, you might first think of putting up a multiband vertical antenna. However, without a large number of wires (*radials*) you might get better results with a simple horizontal or vertical dipole.

Beyond your local area, perhaps 20 or 30 miles, antenna polarization is not very important on HF. Once the RF bounces around a little (off the ionosphere—see Chapter 1), there is no real difference between a signal transmitted vertically or horizontally. At the receiving end, the energy will be mixed with both polarizations.

Perhaps you have read that an antenna with *low-angle radiation*—one that shoots power out as close to the horizontal as possible, such as a very large Yagi with five or six elements—is just the ticket for you to work DX. Unfortunately, if you live in a small valley, surrounded by high hills, much of this power could go into the hills and very little to the outside world. You might be better off with an antenna having a wide vertical pattern, so more RF goes over the tops of the hills.

An understanding of these antenna types and characteristics will allow you to make an informed choice. Then the time and money you spend on an antenna will come close to giving you the results you want.

Measurements, Accuracy and Real Antennas

Jim called. And so did Bob. And Jerry. They didn't call yesterday, nor did they all call last week. Their calls happened over the last few years, and they all told me the same story.

I built a dipole, using the formula in "THE BOOK." I cut the antenna exact, to the nearest $1/8$-inch, strung it between my stepladder and a tree, and *pruned it* (changed the length) until my SWR meter read 1.2:1. Then I put it up between two trees or hung it as an *inverted V* 60 feet in the air. Now the SWR reads 4:1. What happened? Did I mess up the measurements? Was "the book" wrong? Did I make a mistake building it?

The answer to these questions, and several others, lies in the fine print. When you build an antenna, and use the published formulas and lengths, they assume the antenna will be put up free and clear of the ground and any other objects. Free and clear usually means at least $1/2$ to 1 wavelength—on the 80-meter band the antenna should be at least 40 meters ($1/2$ wavelength) or about 130 feet from the ground. The closer to the ground, the less accurate the formula.

The same fine print holds for antenna patterns. "The book" shows one pattern—for a simple dipole the best directions for transmitting and receiving are at right angles to the wire, with very little radiation from the ends of the wire. Mount the dipole close to the ground, and the pattern will really be *omnidirectional*—you will not see much of a difference in any direction!

A couple of basic rules will help you save time and energy:

• Cut a wire antenna to within a few inches of the formula value—we will give you the formula later in this chapter—and then add about 1 foot on each end for a 10-meter antenna. Add about 18 inches for 20 and 40 meters, and 2 feet for 80 meters. This extra wire will allow you to shorten the antenna if you need to do so. Remember, you can always cut off some wire. Soldering wire onto the ends is a little trickier, but can (usually) be done as well.

• Don't waste time adding and subtracting wire to

reduce the SWR, when the antenna is not in its final location. Yes, it can be tedious to raise and lower the antenna between each measurement. Any changes you have to make will be different at different heights and distance from other objects, however.

Parts

No antenna lasts forever. Left outside, with no rain, the 10-meter dipole you just built would probably last a few years. In most areas of the world, an antenna without any weatherproofing would probably last a year or less.

Safety is the primary concern when you plan an antenna. Chapter 7 discusses many of the aspects of safety. Since an antenna is *up*—in the air over people and property—you want to pick the correct material. This does not mean all antenna parts must be stainless steel. It does mean you should follow good practices, and build the antenna is such a way that it can be lowered and inspected periodically.

Wire

The *National Electrical Code* (see the Resources Guide) gives us some guidance on wire to be used for amateur transmitting antennas. It specifies #14 copper-clad steel core or other high-strength wire for antenna spans of less than 150 feet, and #12 for longer. You should read the few applicable paragraphs in the *Code* (available in most libraries), and use it as your guide.

Copper-clad steel is commonly called Copperweld. It has a great advantage of not stretching—once you have cut it to size, it stays the same length.

You can imagine the problem of putting up a 40-meter dipole, carefully adjusting the length, and then seeing the characteristics change, as the antenna stretches longer and longer. Therefore, whatever wire you decide to use, make sure it is non-stretching.

Copperweld does have a disadvantage—normally two people are required to unroll the wire. The steel core makes it act as a coiled spring. You have not experienced true frustration until you cut two 66-foot lengths of Copperweld for an 80-meter dipole, and these two 66-foot springs entangle themselves (and you).

Many hams choose to use non-stretch copper wire obtained from a reputable dealer, and not try to use steel core wire or other hard-drawn wire. Insulated wire can be used, but it is rarely available except as a soft, stretchable material. There is no proof the insulation either helps or hurts the lifespan of the wire, when it is exposed to the weather. Wire with an enameled surface also works well, but you must be sure to remove the enamel before you try to solder the wire. A gentle rubbing with emery cloth usually does a good job of removal. Tin the wire ends (cover them with solder) after removing the enamel.

Insulators

If you wish, you can make your own insulators, as the old-timers used to. First cut a piece of hardwood to the size and shape you want. Then place a pot of paraffin (you may have to melt a few candles to get this paraffin or wax) on the stove, and boil the wood until the paraffin saturates the entire wood block. Be very careful, since liquid paraffin is flammable. Remove the wood, and let it cool. This insulator will probably last a few years.

On the other hand, you could also go to a local radio store such as Radio Shack, or contact one of the nationally advertised ham suppliers, and order a few glass or ceramic insulators. Years ago, I made a few wooden rod insulators to be used as feed-line spacers—just to try the technique. The story of the boiling paraffin (and the stain on the kitchen ceiling) became a family tale, never to be forgotten. Now I buy my insulators.

Fig 3-2A and B show two commonly available insulators for wire antennas. The oblong unit has the advantage of ridges between the two ends, so any build-up of dirt will be less likely to become a conductive path between the wires at each end. The egg-shaped insulator has the advantage of safety. If it cracks and breaks, the two wires remain interlocked, and therefore the antenna will not fall.

The egg-shaped insulator has a further advantage of having the ceramic material *in compression*. Just like concrete and brick, ceramic and glass will take very high

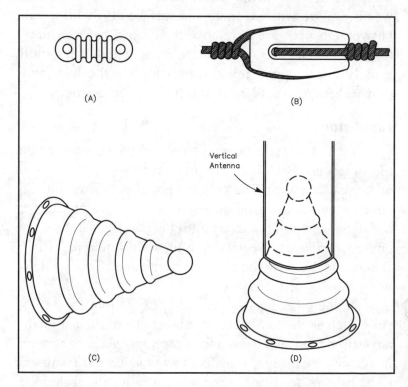

Fig 3-2—Flea markets are a good source of a wide variety of insulators.

forces when compressed. They do not do so well when *under tension;* that is, being pulled out. The pyramid-shaped insulator in Fig 3-2C is often found at flea markets. It was designed to keep the center bolt insulated from the base, so a high voltage wire could be connected to the center bolt.

Occasionally, someone will try to use this insulator to *stand off* a vertical antenna from a conductive mast. The base of the insulator is mounted to the mast, and the antenna to a bolt through the center. Now the insulator is in tension. One day, when a gust of wind comes along, the insulator could be stressed to the point of splitting, and your antenna could fly off!

The final insulator (Fig 3-2D) is in compression, and some hams have actually used soda bottles for the base insulator of a vertical antenna. All should be well, as long as the antenna is guyed to stay vertical, and no sideways force is placed on the top of the insulator.

Hardware

The primary advantage of using good quality galvanized fittings or stainless steel hardware is not, as you may imagine, that they last a long time. It is their lack of corrosion. You can disassemble them and inspect the antenna periodically. Left alone, without periodic checking, all antennas will fall down eventually. Trying to save a few dollars on hardware means you will have to spend a great deal of time trying to remove corroded hardware, and replacing it when you periodically check your antenna. It also means the hardware will fail more quickly.

Feed Lines and Guy Wire

For information on picking feed lines, see Chapter 5. Guy wire and antenna supports are discussed in Chapter 6.

Long Wires—Throw a Piece of Wire Out the Window

Actually, that is the way it works. Many hams start their careers on HF by listening or *SWL*ing. (For more information on short-wave listening see the Resources Directory.)

Their first antenna is a piece of wire (any old length—a *random length* wire), laid around the edge of the room or tossed out the window. It is a natural question to ask: "Can I use my random length wire for transmitting?" The answer is yes—but it is going to take a little more work to make it an efficient ham HF antenna.

Long wire antennas are strictly defined as wires with one end connected to the transmitter or receiver, and with a length of at least two or three wavelengths. Often hams will call any wire—of any length—a "long wire" antenna.

A long wire antenna has several advantages. It is

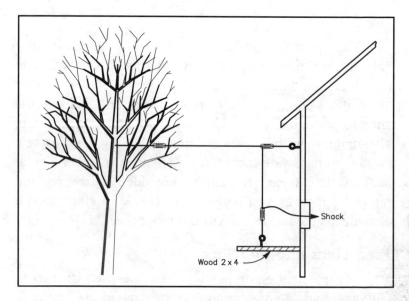

Fig 3-3—Connect the long wire to your shack with insulated, flexible wire. Keep all wires out of the reach of people and pets.

simple, inexpensive, unobtrusive and works! However, it works only as well as its location and length allow. Place 20 feet of wire close to the ground and it will work, but not well. Use 100 feet of wire, strung from your home to a 50-foot tree, and it will work very well.

A good long wire antenna installation is shown in Fig 3-3. The long wire is mounted as high and clear as possible. The vertical part of the wire radiates, so mount this section as far from conducting objects (aluminum downspouts, internal wall wiring) as you can. Also remember safety (Chapter 7). Keep all parts of the wire out of reach! Anyone touching the wire can receive burns from the RF. If you run the wire from a basement or first floor location, position it or cover it with a nonconductor, so no one can touch it.

The insulators and wire types have already been discussed. Equally important is the ground system. Take a look at Fig 3-4. The battery supplies the power to light the

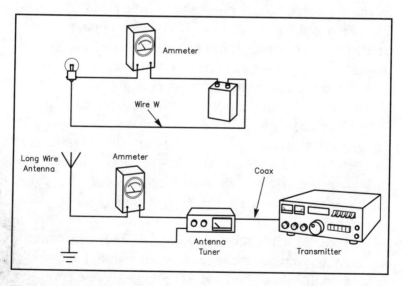

Fig 3-4—A good ground system is very important when you use a long wire antenna. It "completes the circuit."

bulb, and the ammeter measures the current flowing in the circuit. Now suppose you removed the wire labeled W, and replaced it with a very high value resistor. The light goes off, and the ammeter will read almost zero. If you replaced the ammeter with a more sensitive instrument, you might get a reading of a few microamperes. But this current is not enough to light the bulb.

Now look at the bottom of the figure. The battery has been replaced with a transmitter and antenna tuner, which has two output terminals (just as the battery did). One terminal is connected to the antenna, and the other to a ground connection. If you measure the antenna current with a good ground connection, you would see a relatively large current. A poor ground connection would act just like the resistor in the previous example. Therefore, if you want a long wire antenna to work well, you must have a good ground connection.

One practical approach is to tie together as much metal as you can reach. Water pipes and heating pipes are a good start. First make sure there are no connecting pipe sections of PVC or other plastics. Then run a wire, as short as possible, to a ground rod driven into the earth. An 8-foot ground rod is traditional, but very few hams have ever been able to sink this rod the full 8 feet in hard or rocky soil.

Caution: *Some printed material suggests surrounding ground rods with copper sulfate or other chemicals to make the ground more conductive. This is not environmentally friendly, illegal in many areas, and can cause problems with plants, animals and underground water sources.*

Make the wire connecting your rig to the ground rod as large as you can manage. Several parallel lengths of copper braid, taken from old RG-8 coax, is one approach. Don't connect anything to your home power-line grounds (neutral wires) or wire (BX) shields. In addition to safety problems, you will probably induce RF into your house wiring, and cause all sorts of interference problems.

Yes, you may be on the third floor, or perhaps cannot drive a ground rod in further than 2 feet. These are real situations, and one result may be the poorer performance of a long wire antenna. Hopefully, the difference is not critical.

A second result may be RF floating through the shack. You can get little burns as you touch various metal cases. Chapter 5 discusses this problem and the use of *artificial grounds*.

The final element in Fig 3-4 is the tuner. It should be capable of connecting your rig, with a coax cable output, to a single wire. Most tuners can accomplish this, but occasionally the length of the wire and the band selected conspire to prevent the tuner from being adjusted properly. Your choice here is either to change bands or lengthen or shorten the wire by 5 or 10 feet. Chapter 5 discusses tuners for matching antennas.

Another approach to solving the grounding problem is shown in Fig 3-5. A network of wires is used in place of a physical ground connection. These wires, sometimes called a *counterpoise,* are closer to the ground and act as the second conductor in place of the ground. Some hams prefer to put the counterpoise directly on the ground, or bury it close to the surface. Others say they can show better performance if the counterpoise is hung several feet above the ground.

A minimum size for a single counterpoise wire is a length of $^1/_4$ wavelength. Fig 3-5A shows a single wire approach and B a four wire approach. Each of the four wires is $^1/_4$ wavelength long. The four wire approach will give you much better performance in most cases.

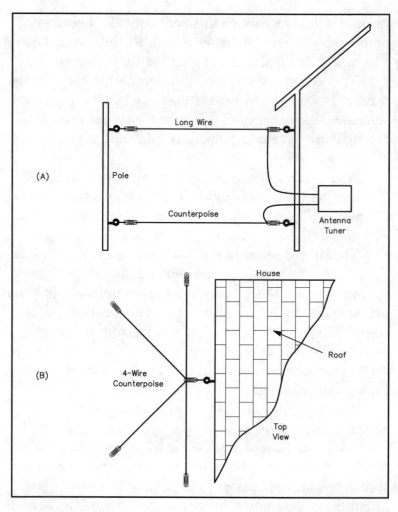

Fig 3-5—A counterpoise acts in the place of a ground connection.

For most installations, safety dictates the location of the counterpoise. A wire 5 feet above the ground can be very dangerous to anyone walking in the area. Raising it to 10 feet is acceptable, but the antenna itself should be as high above the counterpoise as possible. There is no hard and fast rule. On the 10-meter band a separation of 20 feet may be acceptable, while on 80 meters the minimum acceptable distance for reasonable performance may be 40 or 50 feet. You can try experimenting with the number of and lengths of the counterpoise wires. You will get very different results with different choices.

Real Long Wires

A piece of wire, with a length of several wavelengths, is a favorite ham antenna. Unlike a shorter random length wire, it usually has both favored directions (off the ends) and some gain as compared to a dipole. Other hams prefer this antenna, mounted low (10 feet from the ground) for receiving only. Often the noise level picked up on this antenna is less than from an antenna mounted much higher. While the low antenna may not work well for transmitting, it allows you to hear stations that otherwise are buried in the noise. However, you will have to use a second, separate antenna for transmitting.

Safety Once More

It is very tempting, especially with random wire antennas, to believe you could run the wire further or higher, if you could just cross that power wire or line drop to your home. Remember, wires fall down. If your antenna falls across the power line, and you touch your rig, the result could be disastrous.

Verticals and Ground Planes—The Good and the Not so Good

"A vertical antenna is omnidirectional and has a low angle of radiation. It is very good for working DX."

"A vertical antenna is omnidirectional. It radiates equally poorly in all directions."

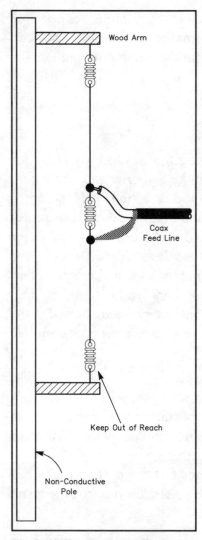

Fig 3-6—For best results, keep the feed line at right angles to the dipole.

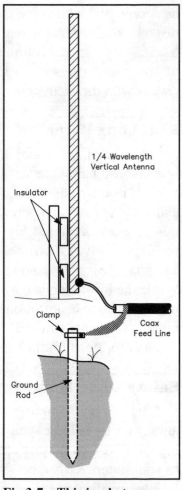

Fig 3-7—This is what many hams visualize when you say "ground plane antenna," but you don't want to build it this way! See text.

These are two very common statements about vertical antennas. They contradict each other, and they are both true. Once you understand how they can be both true and contradictory, you will understand how to decide if a vertical antenna is the right choice for you—and if so, which vertical antenna.

The simple dipole we built, if hung from your home to a nearby tree, is horizontal. The wire runs parallel to the Earth. A vertical antenna has a radiating element that is perpendicular to the Earth, or vertical. If you take our dipole and mount it standing off from a pole (Fig 3-6) it is now a vertical antenna. There is no reason you cannot do this—as long as the pole is nonconductive. If you want to try it, just keep the lower end out of the reach of people and pets. When you transmit, there may be a very high RF voltage on the end of the dipole.

A more conventional vertical antenna has a radiating element $\frac{1}{4}$ wavelength long (Fig 3-7). It is fed by a length of 50-ohm coax and uses a rod, hammered into the ground, as the *second wire* we spoke of before. This is the very basic quarter-wave vertical antenna, often called a *ground plane antenna*. But before you run out and start pounding ground rods, read a little more and get the rest of the story!

Most vertical antennas use a real or synthesized *ground plane*. An ideal ground plane is a very large sheet of metal—imagine a perfect conductor—under the antenna. Fig 3-8A shows a dipole, and B shows half of the dipole with a ground plane. The receiving station cannot tell the difference. We say the ground plane provides an *image antenna*, which in this case is an imaginary quarter-wavelength long element. This image replaces the lower quarter-wave radiator of the original dipole.

The ground plane must be conductive and very big in comparison to the wavelength. Now read that sentence

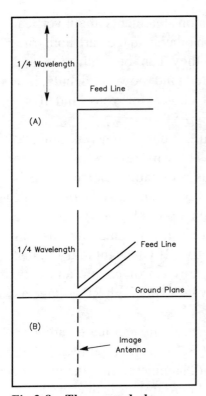

Fig 3-8—The ground plane must be very large—ideally several wavelengths in each direction—to provide a good image.

again. Often, the poor performance of a vertical antenna is caused by the lack of a good ground plane. For example, you can replace the ground plane with 100 or so radial wires or *radials*, each cut to one-quarter wavelength. This produces a very good ground plane. Reduce the number of radials to two or three and the antenna will work, but not as well as one with many radials or a good ground plane.

The Most Common Vertical is the Quarter-Wave Ground Plane

The quarter-wave ground plane antenna is a favorite because it is easy and inexpensive to build and test. In fact, you are probably better off building it than discussing it. There are two parts to it—the vertical radiator and the ground plane. The length of the vertical radiator is given by the formula:

Length in feet = (234)/frequency in MHz

A typical ground plane, with radials, is shown in Fig 3-9. The radials can be horizontal or at an angle as shown. Changing from the horizontal to an angle will change the

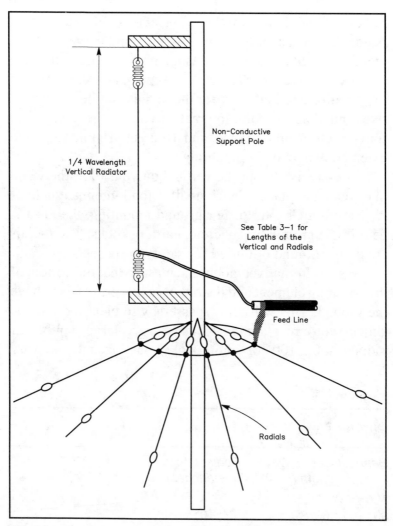

Fig 3-9— Radials are a substitute for a solid ground plane. Use as many as possible, but keep them out of reach.

way the antenna matches the feed line. Often, this angle is not picked, but is a result of how and where you mount the antenna. Generally the radials are 2 or 3% longer than the radiator. Table 3-1 provides lengths of the radiator and radials at the center of the Novice/Tech Plus and other bands. The mast in the figure is nonconductive, such as wood. The radiating element is a length of wire, cut to the dimension given in Table 3-1. You can use you own imagination and ingenuity for the radials. While you would like a hundred or more, in practice you can get away with four—eight would be nice, and 16 great. The mast should extend down to allow mounting.

If you wish to put the vertical on your roof, the wood mast can be placed in a small tripod mount, such as discussed in Chapter 6. For ground mounting, the mast is held in the ground by concrete, earth or rocks. The radials are on the ground or buried for safety purposes.

As an alternative, mount the mast so that the bottom of the radiating element and the radials are about 10 feet above the ground. This will allow passersby to clear the radials. Unless you are planning to use a very large number of radials—50, 100 or more—or your ground is very

Table 3-1

Quarter-Wave Vertical Length

Band	Quarter-Wave Length (λ/4)[1]	Radial Length (feet/inches)
160	123' 2"	126' 4"
80[2]	63' 3"	64' 10"
40[2]	32' 10"	33' 8"
30	23' 1"	23' 8"
20	16' 6"	16' 11"
17	12' 11"	13' 3"
15[2]	11' 1"	11' 4"
12	9' 5"	9' 7"
10[2]	8' 3"	8' 6"

[1]Use this length for each half of a dipole
[2]Novice/Tech Plus band segment

conductive, such as a salt marsh—you are probably better off mounting four (or more) radials clear and high off the ground.

Use your imagination. I had a 20-meter ground plane on the peak of my roof, with no visible radials. I ran a short section of braid from the coax shield through the roof. I twisted the end of the braid to the ends of 20 pieces of 18-inch wide aluminum foil, stapled to the underside of the shingle (nonconductive) roof. Thus, my antenna had 20 radials **under the roof in the attic**. Every radial was not straight—some ran under the roof up to the house eaves, and then along the attic floor. The antenna was inconspicuous, and no one noticed all that aluminum foil in the attic!

A multiband version of a quarter-wave ground plane is drawn in Fig 3-10. Again, the lengths are taken from Table 3-1. Don't hesitate to try two or three bands at once. A set of three or four radials for each band is desirable. The radials are made from TV rotator cable. Common flat rotator cable comes in four or five-conductor versions. In the two-band version shown only two conductors are needed, so double up by tying two of the four conductors together on each band.

Radials—How Many and Where?

Earlier in this chapter we saw that the radials for a ground plane antenna were a substitute for a large, conducting plane of metal. Since it is not practical to cover the ground with a metal sheet one or two wavelengths long on an HF band, radials are the usual solution. Often this leads to a question: "How many should there be and where should they be?"

Let's look at a few general guidelines:

• If your radials are going to be on or just under the ground surface, you will need about eight of them.

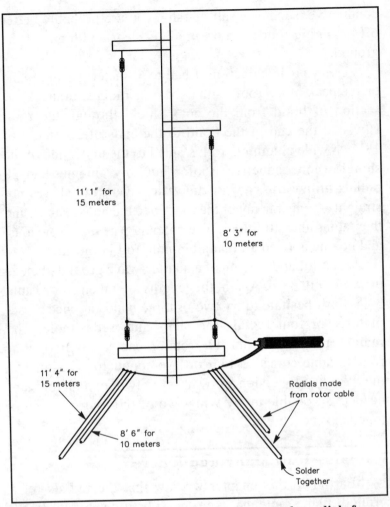

11' 1" for
15 meters

8' 3" for
10 meters

11' 4" for
15 meters

8' 6" for
10 meters

Radials made
from rotor cable

Solder
Together

Fig 3-10—Rotor cable is a convenient way to make radials for multiband ground plane antennas. At a minimum, use at least four radials for each band.

Commercial broadcasters use over 100 radials, but this only results in a very slightly better-radiated signal—a few per cent better.

 • If you mount your radials well over the ground, then

Fig 3-11—This is the view from the boom of Dom Grande, I8UDB's antenna. It is a 3-element, 80-meter Yagi, mounted 490 feet above the Tyrrhenian Sea.

four radials will provide a reasonable efficiency. One reason to use over four is, perhaps, to smooth out the omnidirectional pattern of the antenna. The pattern, which is really a picture of how much power goes out in each direction, is often more sensitive to the ground surrounding the antenna than the exact number of radials.

Commercial Vertical Antennas—Look Before you Leap

There are many good commercial vertical antennas on the market. Typical is the multiband Cushcraft R7 in Fig 3-12. Unfortunately, for every well-designed vertical available, there is one that is not so good. Here are a few hints you should follow for picking a commercial vertical antenna.

• Read the product reviews in *QST*. Each December issue contains an index of the products tested during the past year.

• Gain figures are misleading. "10 dB gain!" 10 dB over what—the proverbial wet noodle? That is one reason *QST* does not carry gain figures in their advertisements.

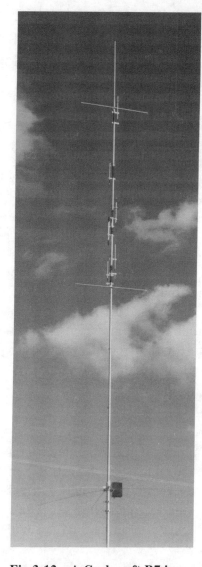

Fig 3-12—A Cushcraft R7 is a multiband vertical antenna. You can mount it either on the ground or on the roof. It does not require radials (see text). *(Photo courtesy of Cushcraft)*

- Be suspicious. If the advertisement says "Needs no ground plane," and the manufacturer sells an "optional set of radials," find out why!

- Ignore names. Just as "Regal," "LTX," or "Gran Torismo" does not give you any real information on a car, "Lounden-Boomer III" and "Star-Bright" does not tell you anything about an antenna.

- Unfortunately, your friend's recommendation of the antenna he or she just bought may not be a good reason for you to go out and buy the same antenna. It is very difficult to evaluate just one antenna at home.

- Commercial multi-band antennas do have some good features. As their name suggests, they cover several bands. Check if the model you pick covers all the bands of interest to you. Normally, it is not efficient to design an antenna for the HF (80 to 10-meter) bands that also covers either 6 meters or

2 meters. You would usually be better off with a separate antenna for the VHF bands.

- Most commercial antennas allow you to use any length of 50-ohm coax (see Chapter 5 for a discussion on selecting coax). Check if the model you are considering requires a specific type, length or section of coax as a *matching section*—to allow you to connect normal 50-ohm coax to the antenna without an antenna tuning unit.

Vertical Half-Wavelength Dipoles—Worth Considering

Earlier in this chapter (Fig 3-6) a standard dipole was mounted vertically, with the feed line coming from the center of the dipole to the shack. Often, this is not a convenient arrangement.

There is another option. Center feed the dipole, as you would any normal half-wavelength dipole, but bring the feed line out at one end (Fig 3-13). Two lengths of tubing— lightweight TV mast is a good choice—are cut to the dimensions of Table 3-1. If you use several lengths, wedged together, they should be fastened with three or four non-corroding sheet metal screws, to ensure they stay in electrical contact. An alternative to TV mast is electrical conduit. Pick a size that allows the coax to run through the center and clear any sheet metal screws.

Rig a center insulator from PVC or other nonconducting pipe to fit over the ends or inside the ends of the two elements. As shown, the elements are separated by two inches. A hole in the center allows the coax feed line to come out of the pipe. Next to the center section there is an alternative feed connection arrangement. The coax center conductor and shield are fastened to the two lengths of pipe with sheet metal screws or hose clamps. If you use sheet metal screws, be sure they are as short as possible, so they do not cut into the coax in the pipe.

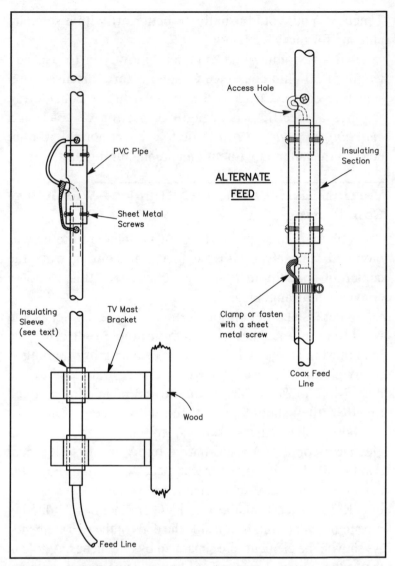

Fig 3-13—Since the feed line comes out one end, this vertical dipole makes a neat rooftop installation.

The end of the coax should be weatherproofed as described in Chapter 6. It is also a good idea to spray each of the sheet metal screws with a weatherproof coating or plastic spray, to preserve them.

The lower section of the dipole fits in two standard TV mast brackets. These brackets are mounted on a non-conducting piece of wood. An insulating piece of plastic, inserted between the mast and brackets, also can be used.

The feed line, as shown, exits the bottom of the dipole. This, of course, is the advantage of making such a vertical dipole. You can mount it on your roof and easily run the feed line through the bottom of the antenna. Unfortunately, this is also the disadvantage. There will be some distortion of the radiation pattern. Most probably there also will be some SWR problems, since the dipole is now not really balanced. One side is much closer to the feed line than the other. It may be necessary to add a *choke balun* (see Chapter 5) to reduce the SWR, and eliminate any RF energy that could be floating around the shack.

Grounds, Matching and Feeding

Two other popular variations of vertical antennas are illustrated in Fig 3-14. In A, the vertical radiating element—any convenient size but usually as long as possible—is surrounded by as many radials as possible. The radials are as long and as many as you want to install. Located directly at the base of the vertical is an antenna tuner. It is in an insulated, weatherproof enclosure. All controls and the case is insulated from contact with your hand. A 1:1 balun may be inserted **at the input of the tuner**, and connected to the transmitter by any standard coax. With the proper tuner adjustments, you can use this arrangement on any band, while having a low SWR at the far end of the coax.

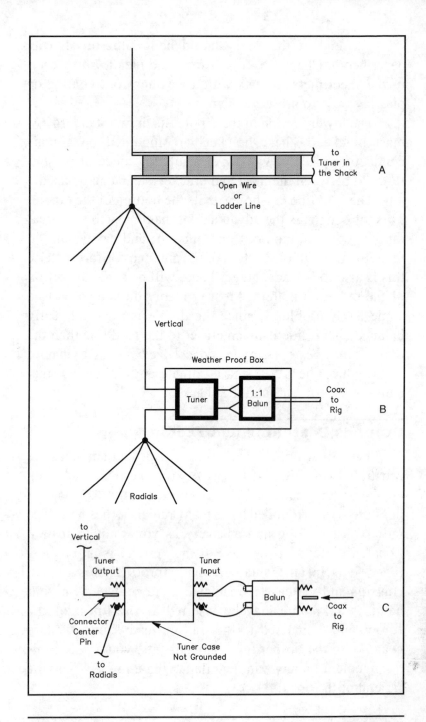

← **Fig 3-14—The tuner here is *hot*. Do not connect the tuner case to anything. All controls and the case must be insulated. If you use open wire line, you can place the tuner near the shack, which is more convenient. However, open wire line cannot be buried or hidden, and passersby must be protected from making contact.**

A similar arrangement is in B, but perhaps a little more convenient. The antenna and radials are fed by open-wire line. The usual precautions must be taken to keep people or animals from making contact with the antenna, radials or transmission line. The tuner is now mounted at the window of the shack, and thus it is a bit more convenient to operate. A balun also will be required (see Chapter 5).

The Many-Flavored Dipole

If I had to have just one antenna—for just one HF band or several—what would I chose? This is a very common question, and many hams would answer "a dipole." *BC*— before coax—a standard antenna consisted of a dipole, as long as possible, fed with homebrewed open-wire feed line. In the shack the feed line was connected to an antenna tuner. This tuner was designed specifically for balanced line. The high SWR often found on the line was not important, since the line had very low loss.

Later, hams changed to the convenience of coax, and the dipole was now restricted to a specific length for each band to reduce the SWR. These dipoles, cut to a specific length for each frequency, are called *resonant dipoles*. This approach was necessary since the coax was not low loss, and considerable power could be lost in long coax runs. Today, with the availability of ladder line and low-loss coax, hams are rethinking this approach.

If you live in a valley, and want to talk to friends from 20 to 300 miles away consistently and dependably, the dipole is for you. Is DX your main interest? If you have a limited budget, you may be better off sticking with the inexpensive dipole, but mounting it as high as possible. Spend your money on higher supports such as a tower, and you might be able to add a better (more expensive) antenna later.

At this point you should have a good image of a dipole. It is $1/2$ wavelength long. Therefore, if you are thinking about 80 meters, a dipole is about 40 meters long. There are (approximately—very approximately) 3 feet to a meter, so an 80-meter half wavelength dipole is about 3 times 40 or about 120 feet long. Now when anyone says "dipole," you should have a mental picture of an end insulator, a length of wire, a center insulator with a feed line, the other half of the wire, and the other end insulator. Given a band, you can calculate the approximate length of the quarter-wave vertical, which is the same as each half of a dipole.. When you are ready to build a dipole, Table 3-1 will give you the actual length of each half of the dipole.

Earlier we used the formula *length = 234/(frequency in MHz)* to calculate the length of a quarter-wave vertical, which is the same length as each half of a dipole. In fact, the value (234) is not exact for every application. That is why we suggested adding a foot or two to each end of the dipole to allow for adjustment. Except for the effect on SWR, some tests have shown that a dipole can be shortened by almost 50% without seriously affecting the strength of the signal at the far (receiving) end. Use ladder line or a short piece of low-loss coax (see Chapter 5), and a short dipole will work almost as well as a full size one.

Actually, the radiation pattern of any antenna is affected by its distance from the ground. The nice, symmetrical patterns of dipole shown in some books are not included here, because in many cases they do not exist.

They are theoretical—they exist only in *free space,* where there is neither ground nor anything near the dipole. Thus, unless your dipole is several wavelengths above the ground (can you put up a 2×80 or 160-meter-high tower?), the theoretical pattern and carefully calculated lengths can be far different in reality.

Real Dipoles

The basic elements of a practical dipole are sketched in Fig 3-15. The length of each side of the dipole comes from Table 3-1, with one foot or so added for pruning on 10

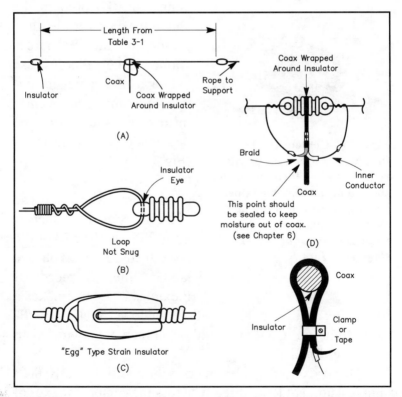

Fig 3-15—Follow these construction details, and your dipole will stay in good condition for many years!

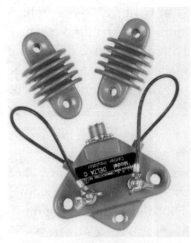

Fig 3-16—Commercial center insulators and baluns usually require a PL-259 connector on the end of the coax feed line. *(Photo A courtesy of Alpha Delta Communications, Inc; photo B courtesy of Palomar Engineers, Inc)*

meters, and two feet on 80 meters. A clamp or tape will hold the coax feed line in place around the center insulator. Be careful—don't squeeze the coax to the point where the coax is deformed internally. Clamp it or tape it just tightly enough to hold it.

This dipole uses coax as the feed line, without a connector. To prepare the end of the coax see the illustration in the Resources Guide. Other dipoles use baluns as the center insulator, or commercial center insulators such as the one made by Alpha-Delta (Fig 3-16). Also see Chapter 5. Commercial center connectors require the use of a coax connector, such as a PL-259, on the end of the coax feed line. If you use ladder line, a piece of Plexiglas or Lexan makes a fine center insulator. The width of the lower section (vertical portion in Fig 3-17) should be an inch or so wider than the ladder line.

One trick used by old-timers is the addition of a 10,000-ohm resistor, soldered directly across the center insulator of the dipole. On the ground, an ohmmeter connected across

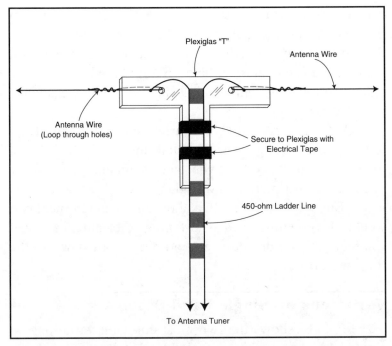

Fig 3-17—Make your own center insulator for ladder line from Plexiglas or any tough, weather-resistant plastic.

the feed line should measure this value of 10,000 ohms. A short circuit means the feed line or connector is shorted, and an open circuit means the feed line is broken. The resistor has no effect on the antenna or the SWR.

Pruning

Your dipole is built. You have raised it to its final position, and it is time to see if it is built correctly. If you own or can borrow any of the antenna test instruments described in Chapter 5, they will tell you directly—read the instruction manual!—if the antenna is too long or too short. If your only test instrument is an SWR meter (or SWR bridge), then you must make several measurements at different frequencies. If the SWR is better (lower) toward the top end of the band (higher in frequency than you wish), the antenna is too short. A better SWR at the low end—the antenna is too long. Lengthening and shortening the antenna is called *pruning*.

On 80 meters (and 160) a variation in SWR from 1.2:1 to 4:1 across the band is not unusual. Just prune the antenna to give the best SWR at the band segment you usually operate. On 40 meters and higher, less of a variation is usual. But before you get all excited, and spend the next two weeks lengthening and shortening the antenna, read Chapter 5. Then decide if any pruning at all is worth the time and effort.

Variations on Single Band Dipoles

Fig 3-18 shows the two most common variations on single band dipoles. The *inverted V* takes its name from its shape. It is simply a dipole with a single center support. The angle between the wires is not critical, although most hams try to keep the arms at least 90° apart. The ends can run close to the ground, but the antenna will be less efficient, and in addition pose a danger to anyone coming in contact with it.

The length of the inverted V tends to be a bit longer— from 5 to 10%—than the length of a standard dipole. Start off with the dipole lengths in Table 3-1 plus 10%, and then prune it if necessary.

The other standard variation is the *sloper*. Again the name is taken from the shape. It is a dipole with just one end elevated. The angle is not critical, and the claim is often made that the antenna favors the direction shown by the small arrow. This "favored direction" depends heavily on the ground underneath and near the antenna. Don't bet on it

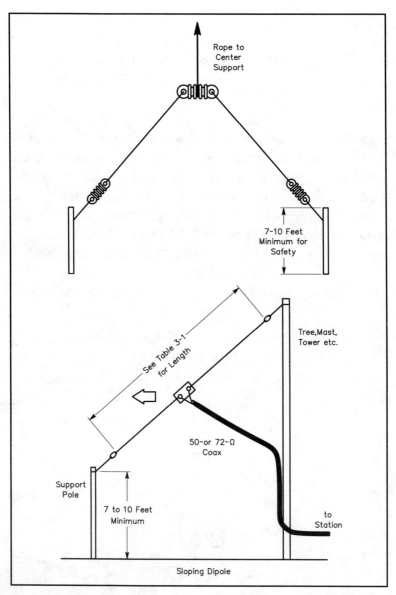

Fig 3-18—The inverted V and the sloper are two popular variations of the half-wave dipole. They need less space than a horizontal dipole.

to give you a big advantage in that direction. Customarily the coax shield is connected to the lower element, as shown in the sketch, but this is just a custom. Once more, keep the end of the sloper out of anyone's reach. RF burns are very nasty!

Shorty dipoles are another common variation. If you cut a dipole as much as 30 to 50% shorter than the values in the table, the lower efficiency of the dipole often does not affect your signal very much. The primary effect of cutting the dipole short is to change the way the dipole matches the transmission line. The SWR goes up. Therefore, if you use open wire line, such as in Fig 3-19, or very low loss coax, a shorty dipole can be used on almost any band. Be careful— under some combinations of dipole length, feed line length and frequency, very high voltages may be present. If you

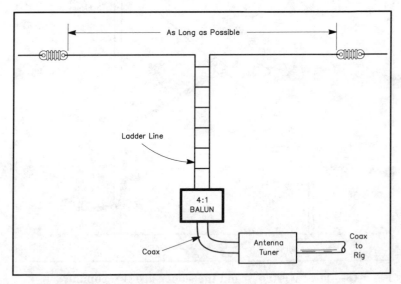

Fig 3-19—An all-band dipole can be cut to as little as 50% of the length of a conventional half wave dipole, on the lowest band you wish to operate. The key is the use of a low-loss feed line, such as ladder line or open wire line.

are using an antenna tuner designed for low power work, these voltages may be enough to arc within your tuner.

Harmonic dipoles take advantage of the fact that a dipole works well not only on the frequency it was cut to, but also on odd harmonics (such as the third harmonic) of this frequency. In reality, this only affects hams who wish to operate on both 40 and 15 meters. It means that if you cut a dipole for 7 MHz, it will also give you a good match (low SWR) on 3×7 or 21 MHz. Thus, one dipole serves both the 40 and 15-meter bands. If you decide to prune this antenna, prune it on 21 MHz. It will then probably be acceptable on 7 MHz.

If you don't quite have room for the 66-foot long 40-meter dipole there is no reason to quit yet. Try a *bent dipole*. The ends are bent to fit the space available (Fig 3-20). You might have to make one side longer (or shorter) than the other to compensate for their physical unbalance, but you will end up with a perfectly good dipole.

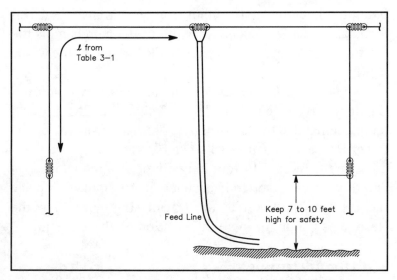

Fig 3-20—Not enough room? Bend the ends of the dipole to fit.

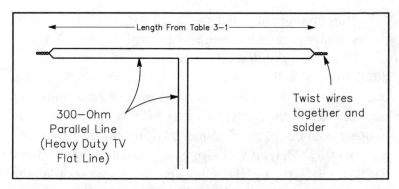

Fig 3-21—This folded dipole is made from 300-ohm flat line (TV feed line). Connect it to your antenna tuner through a 4:1 balun.

Folded dipoles are often used to keep the SWR lower over the full width of the 40-meter and higher ham bands (Fig 3-21). The folded dipole is made of 300-ohm parallel wire transmission line. For low power applications (100-watts or less) ordinary TV flat lead will do just fine. The end of the transmission line must be connected to a 4:1 balun to match the coax output from your transmitter. Unfortunately, on 80 meters the width of the ham band is too large for this antenna to keep the SWR low across the whole band.

Inductively loaded dipoles are another way to allow a dipole to have an electrical length longer than the physical length demanded by the formulas. This is very handy on the lower HF bands, such as 160 meters, where very few hams are able to erect a 246-foot long dipole. An inductance—a coil of wire—is inserted in each leg of the dipole to replace the electrical properties of the missing wire. See the Resources Guide for more information on these antennas.

Multiband Dipoles

All right, you know almost any dipole can be used on

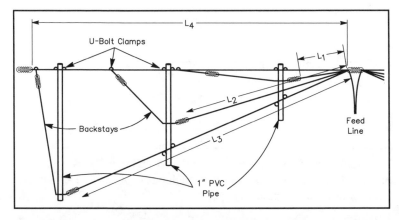

Fig 3-22—L1 is 8 feet 3 inches for 10 meters, L2 is 11 feet 1 inch for 15 meters, L3 is 16 feet 6 inches for 20 meters and L4 is 32 feet 10 inches for 40 meters. Remember to add an extra foot or two on each side for pruning.

any band if you also use low-loss feed lines and an antenna tuner. But you don't want to bother with an antenna tuner! Well, many hams have had the same feeling, and there are many dipoles you can build (or buy) that give you multiple bands, one transmission line and no tuner.

I used the unit shown in Fig 3-22 for many years. It was nicknamed "the eagle catcher," in answer to my neighbor's question: "What the heck is it?" It was not inconspicuous, but it did work well on 40, 20, 15 and 10. I used it because I had exactly one and only one set of trees that would support a dipole as high as possible, and I wanted to put all my dipoles as high as possible. So I did!

The insulating sections were 1-inch PVC pipe. Only the top element (the 40-meter dipole) was made from hard drawn wire, since it was the only one that provided structural support. The other elements were made from stranded copper wire. The "backstays" shown kept the

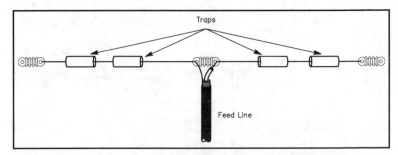

Fig 3-23—The traps make this dipole act electrically as a resonant dipole (as though cut to the lengths of Table 3-1) on three bands simultaneously.

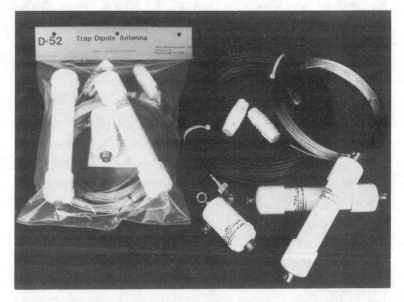

Fig 3-24—Spi-Ro offers this 5-band dipole kit, including all wire, traps and insulators. *(Photo courtesy of Spi-Ro Manufacturing)*

elements for the higher bands under tension, and were fastened to the 40-meter elements with guy wire U-bolt clamps. After hoisting it in place, the 40-meter element was pruned first, followed by the 20-meter element, and then the next two higher bands. With only 75 feet of good quality coax feed line, I did not bother to get the SWR lower than 3:1 at its worst point. For the most part the SWR was less than 2:1 over most of the bands.

Trap dipoles are another approach to using one dipole on several bands. Fig 3-23 is a sketch of one such dipole. The traps usually consist of an inductor in parallel with a heavy-duty capacitor, contained in a weatherproof case. Other approaches use a section of coiled coax as the trap.

The commercial trap dipole shown in Fig 3-24 comes as a complete kit. This one is made by Spi-Ro Manufacturing, and works on all bands from 80 to 10 meters. Several other multiband dipoles are discussed later in this chapter in the section on "Brand Name Antennas."

Rotatable Dipoles—Not as Complex as you Might Think

First go out and buy a rotator. Then find a welding shop and ask them if they can weld aluminum tubing. Lastly, go to your nearest aircraft supply store, and buy 250 feet of lightweight aircraft tubing, guaranteed to last 85 years under hurricane-force winds!

Is that what you think of, when someone suggests you build a rotatable dipole? Perhaps you can do it just a little easier, as suggested in Fig 3-25. This rotatable dipole uses two lengths of electrical conduit, cut for 10 meters according to Table 3-1. A 3-foot length of "2 by 4" wood holds the elements in place. Seal the wood with a good quality outdoor primer and paint.

You might be lucky enough to find a boat trailer bearing that will fit snugly around the pipe mast. A set of TV mast stand-off brackets, fastened to your house or a pole, hold the bearings. If you can't find bearings, just don't tighten the mast clamps very hard. Since the total weight of the assembly is not great, there is no need for machine precision.

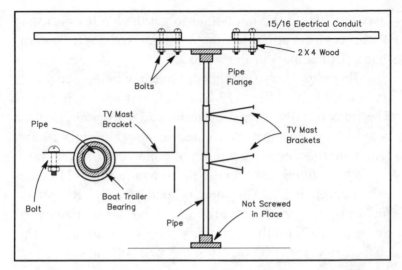

Fig 3-25—Sections of electrical conduit are the elements of this rotatable dipole. To rotate it, use your muscles!

Since no rotator is used, you might ask: "How do I rotate it?" The answer is the *Armstrong method.* Grab the mast with your hand and use your strong arm to turn it! You can invent your own method of keeping track of the direction of the dipole.

Does it work? Yes. Has it been used before? Hundreds of times. Can you improve it? Sure! You could run a bicycle chain to a toothed gear on the mast, with the other end of the chain in your shack. You could… You could do dozens of things to improve it. They could be both fun and practical. Just use your imagination.

Yagis and Quads—Many Advantages

There it is, silhouetted against the sky—a thing of beauty. The dream of many, sometimes achievable and sometimes elusive. That's how many hams feel about Yagi antennas, such as the one in Fig 3-26. What is their prime

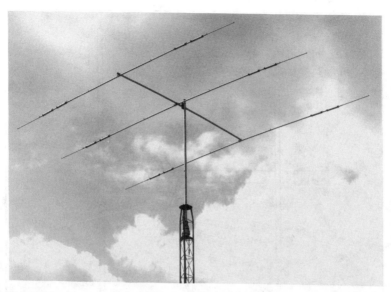

Fig 3-26—The Cushcraft A3S multiband Yagi is a beautiful sight against the sky—with performance to match. *(Photo courtesy of Cushcraft)*

advantage? Gain—it is as though you were using higher power, and the station you are talking to is also using higher power. Disadvantages? Cost plus the problems in placing a large structure high in the sky.

Yagis, or *beams* as they are often called, use carefully placed radiators to focus the energy sent to the antenna. It is not much different from using a lens system on a flashlight. Energy that would otherwise go up and to the back (away from the station you wish to work), now is redirected toward the front. The basic terms you will hear over and over are shown in Fig 3-27. Three elements are shown; therefore, this is called a 3-element Yagi. One element is connected to a feed line—this is the *driven element*. All elements in front of the driven element (and they are usually slightly shorter than the driven element) are

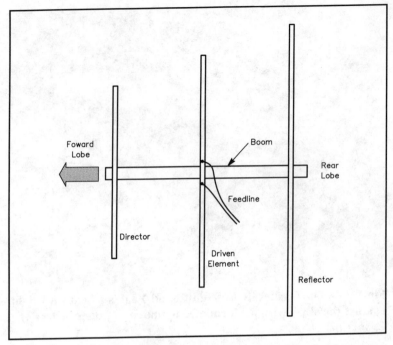

Fig 3-27—All 3-element Yagis (or beams) have these basic parts.

called *directors*—they direct the beam forward. The other element shown (behind the driven element) is a *reflector*— it reflects energy forward. Reflectors are usually slightly longer than the driven element.

To qualify as a Yagi, at least two elements are required. Thus there will be a driven element, and either a reflector or director. Often there is more than one director. A Yagi with two directors, a driven element and a single reflector would be a 4-element Yagi.

The focused beam is the front lobe or forward lobe. Naturally to the rear is the rear lobe, and energy leaking out the sides are called—understandably—side lobes.

Each element is roughly the size of a dipole, so you can think of a Yagi as a set of dipoles stacked on a *boom*. In the middle of the boom there is usually a mechanical arrangement to connect the boom to a shaft, so the Yagi can be rotated.

These antennas are usually discussed in terms of *gain,* as compared to a simple dipole. Later in this book (Chapter 5) we will look at power gains and losses, and how this affects our signals. For now, just remember that 3 dB of gain in an antenna is the same as doubling our output power **as measured at the receiving end**, and 6 dB quadruples it. Therefore, suppose you change your antenna from a dipole to a Yagi having a 6 dBd gain. If you are using a transmitter with 100-watts output, your new signal strength from the antenna—as measured at a receiving station in front of the Yagi— is now the same as using $100 \times 2 \times 2 = 400$ watts with your original dipole.

Notice the *d* appended to the abbreviation for decibels, d**B**d. This means the value is *as compared to a dipole.* Sometimes the number will be given as d**B**i. This means it is being compared to an *isotropic source*—a fictitious antenna in free space. This results in numbers higher by 2 or so dB than the dBd comparison would produce. If the gain is given in dB—without any qualification or explanation—there is no way to know just what the number means!

A good, single-band two-element Yagi will have a gain of 4 to 5 dBd. A 3-element Yagi will have a gain of about 7 dBd. But before you get too excited about these gain figures, and how they affect your signal at the receiving end, read Chapter 5 to see the relationship between dB and *S units.* A few dB may be less important than you think.

As you can see from the sketch, there also is a good amount of power leaving the back of the antenna. This is called the *rear lobe,* or back lobe. The ratio of gain from the front lobe to the rear lobe is called the *front-to-back ratio.*

Not only is it a measure of the Yagi's efficiency (the more out the front, the less out the rear), but also is a measure of how much stations transmitting behind you will be attenuated, as you attempt to listen to that weak DX station in front.

If you look carefully at the elements on the Cushcraft Yagi in Fig 3-26, you will see a set of two tubular sections on each half of each element. These are traps—similar to the traps discussed for multiband dipoles. Here the traps provide multiband operation for a Yagi. Unfortunately, all antenna designs contain compromises. Here the addition of traps, to provide the advantage of operation on several bands, results in slightly reduced gain and poorer front-to-back ratio, as compared to a single band Yagi with the same number of elements.

Quads

Quads are a lot of fun. Not only as antennas, but also as the subject of arguments that never seem to end—which is better, a quad or a Yagi? A quad is a Yagi with elements replaced by loops of wire. The length of each half of a Yagi element is approximately $1/4$ wavelength, and therefore each Yagi element is about the size of a $1/2$-wavelength dipole. Quads—named after the original design shape of a four-sided loop (Fig 3-28)—have sides approximately $1/4$ wavelength long, and therefore the total loop is about one full wavelength long.

The loops can be square as in A or be diamond shaped as in B. Feed it on the top, side, corner, bottom or anywhere else you want. The loop can even be 3-sided (C), in which case it is called a *delta quad* or just plain *delta*. The feed point determines the polarization, which as we saw before is not very important for HF antennas.

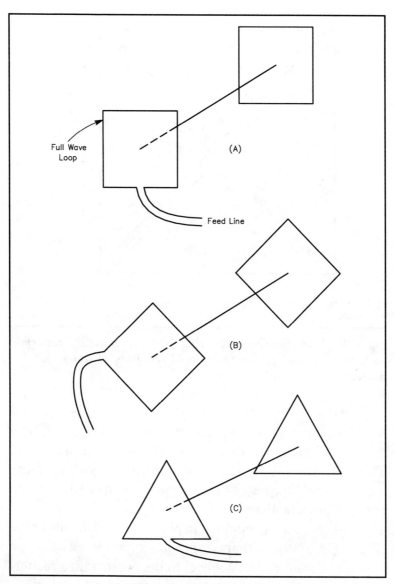

Fig 3-28—A loop's performance is pretty independent of its shape, as long as the sides are close to equal in length.

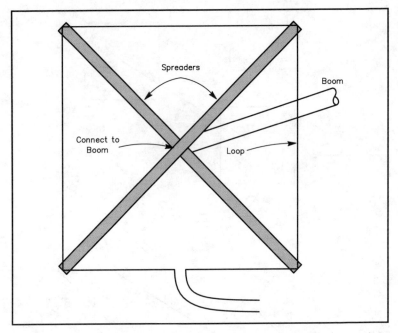

Fig 3-29—Make the spreaders from any nonconductive material, such as wood, fiberglass or bamboo. Fiberglass, of course, lasts longest.

Most quad users feed the loop in the middle of a horizontal element, or at the bottom of the diamond. This results in horizontal polarization. If you feed the loop in the middle of a vertical side it will provide vertical polarization.

The loops are positioned in place of the elements of the Yagis (Fig 3-29). X-shaped *spreaders* hold the wire loops in place. The spreaders connect to the boom with a mounting plate or some arrangements of clamps.

What's the answer to the question: "Which is better, a quad or a Yagi?" To me, they are both the same. It is just a matter of which one is more convenient to build and put in place.

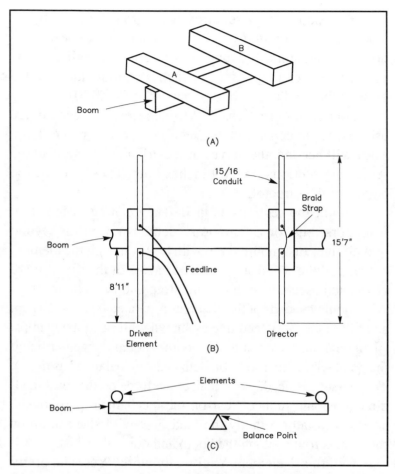

Fig 3-30—A wood boom, two sections of electrical conduit and a few bolts will give you a 2-element 10-meter Yagi.

Let's Build a Yagi

Perhaps not physically, as we did with a dipole at the beginning of this chapter. But we can certainly build it on paper to see what it takes. Then, if you want, you can go to the Resources Guide. There you will find sources to build your own Yagi for whatever band you wish.

This paper Yagi requires two 8-foot-long "2 by 4" wooden beams or *studs* as the boom and the framework to hold the elements. Cut one stud in two and nail it so its center line is exactly 4 feet 11 inches from its mate nailed on the other end of the boom (part A of Fig 3-30).

Four 10-foot sections of $^{15}/_{16}$-inch electrical conduit are used as the elements. Cut two sections 8 feet 11 inches long. They will become the halves of the driven element. Cut the remaining sections 7 feet 9 inches long. These will be the halves of the director.

Mount the sections as in B. They can be fastened on insulators, but for a temporary demonstration, dry wood will do fine. Just mount them with bolts through the element halves and the wood support. The halves of the director are connected together with a braid strap and two clamps.

Mount the ends of the elements separated by a 1-inch gap, and fasten the coax feed line as shown with two pipe clamps. Clamp the mast section to the boom—not at the center but at the point where the forces on both ends are balanced as in (C). This balance is needed to equalize the force on the mast in all directions, and reduce wear on the mechanical parts of the shaft and rotator. Finally the feed line, with slack to allow rotation, is routed along the boom and down the mast.

Will this 2-element Yagi really work? Yes, and pretty well. Many similar antennas were built years ago, before strong, lightweight aluminum tubing was available for the boom. Although it is heavy, it does not require any special parts or tools to build.

Don't Like Wood and Metal? How About Wire?

Wire Yagis are another possibility. They are fun and quick to build, easily modified and work well. If you don't like the result, take out the wire clippers and soldering iron, and try again. They do have a disadvantage—they are usually strung between a couple of trees or poles, and not normally rotated, so they favor only one direction.

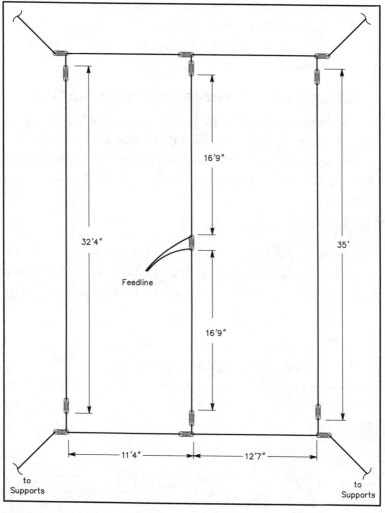

Fig 3-31—This wire 20-meter Yagi has about 7 dBd gain if you can place it at a 40 or 50-foot height. Since it is made of wire you can build it without any special tools. It is worth trying even if you can only put it at 20 or 25 feet.

The element lengths and spacings of a 3-element wire beam are shown in Fig 3-31. Four corner wires or ropes are used to support the assembly. The dimensions shown are for a 3-element 20-meter Yagi. The lengths shown are based on having all wires horizontal. If they are left loose, and droop, the Yagi performance will degrade. As you can see, only wire, insulators and an investment of a few hours are needed to try this one.

Loops—an Interesting Alternative

A loop antenna is just what its name suggests—a complete loop of wire, broken only to attach a feed line. The quad discussed earlier is just a set of loops. A single loop can be used as an antenna. The normal design formula for a loop is:

length (in feet) = 1005/frequency (in MHz)

Table 3-2 contains the lengths for several ham bands, but if you can fit a loop for 80 meters, you can probably use it on all bands up to 10 meters. Feed it with ladder line or

Table 3-2

Full Wave Loop Length (feet/inches)

Band	Length
160	528' 11"
80[1]	271' 7"
40[1]	141' 1"
30	99' 3"
20	70' 11"
17	55' 6"
15[1]	47' 6"
12	40' 4"
10[1]	35' 6"

[1]Novice/Tech Plus band segment

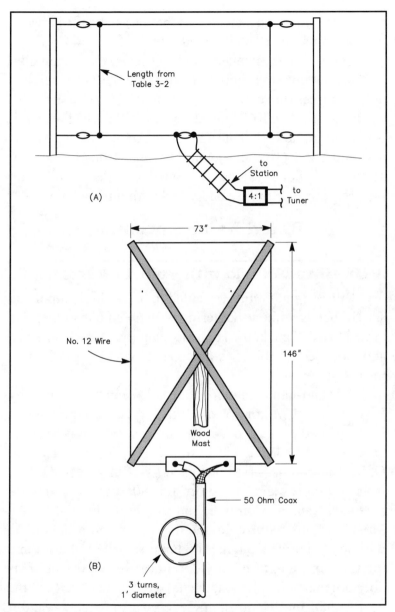

Fig 3-32—Make a full-wave loop for any band. In (A) it is shown mounted vertically, but it also can be mounted horizontally. Brian Beezley, K6STI, designed the small one in (B) for 10 meters. Mount it on a wood pole, 1 inch in diameter, and you can rotate it.

open wire line, and place a 4:1 balun as shown between your antenna tuner and the feed line.

Loops can be mounted either vertically or horizontally. You can mount your loop vertically (Fig 3-32A) when two poles (or trees) are convenient. A smaller version, designed by Brian Beezley, K6STI, is drawn in B. Outlined behind it is a wood framework that supports the loop. This antenna is a single band (10-meter) unit. It rotates on the vertical section of wood. Stand the wire off the wood with insulators, or use dry, sealed wood without insulators.

Brand-Name Antennas

A Multiband Dipole with Built-In Matching

Bill Wright, GØFAH, wanted to use a single dipole on six HF bands without bothering with an antenna tuner. He turned to a design, known to many hams as a *G5RV* antenna, and modified it a bit. The antenna shown in Fig 3-33 was the result.

A brand-name antenna does not mean it was built by Ford, General Motors or any other specific company. It just means there is a person's name, a call sign or some other tag identifying the basic design. In this case, the G5RV antenna was first designed by—surprise!—G5RV. It is a dipole, slightly short for 80 meters, fed with balanced transmission line, and usable on several bands. Most versions require an antenna tuner and a balun. As with most unique designs, the length of the radiator, and the type and length of the feed line, are important. This does not mean that the lengths have to be cut exactly to the nearest half inch. You should exercise some care—and if the published design calls for 41 feet of 450-ohm ladder line, as does GØFAH's version, use 41 feet of 450-ohm ladder line!

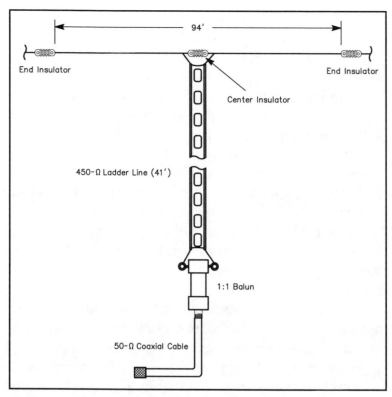

Fig 3-33—94 feet is all you need to fit GØFAH's latest version of the classic G5RV antenna. It works on 80, 40, 20, 17, 12 and 10 meters.

Other Familiar Names

Another brand name antenna, often listed in antenna books, is the *Windom*. It consists of a $1/2$-wavelength long single wire, with a second piece of wire connected offset from the center. This second piece of wire acts as a single-wire feed line. It is not recommended for use today. Hams using this antenna often had problems with RF floating around in their shacks. If you want to use a single wire feed, just put up an end-fed long wire—and remember to have a good ground system.

A variation of a long-wire is the *Beverage* antenna.

You would use it for receiving on 80 and 160 meters. It consists of a long (several wavelengths) wire, mounted close to the ground (Fig 3-34). At the far end, a resistor connects the antenna end to a ground system. It is very inefficient for transmitting, but does a good job on receiving when signal strengths are relatively high (the low HF bands—below 10 MHz), and high noise levels are the problem.

Two long wires, strung in the air in a V shape, form an antenna called—you guessed it—a *V-antenna or V-beam*. Fed at the apex with open wire or ladder line, this antenna can be very directive. Often, each leg of the V is 6 or 8 wavelengths long. These are not small antennas, especially for 40 meters or lower! However, for 10 meters they are an interesting alternative. See the Resources Guide for more information.

A *rhombic* is another alternative to using a Yagi or quad for higher gain. If you own a large piece of real estate, the rhombic—note the shape in Fig 3-35—can provide a good antenna. Although usually designed for one band, with each section 6 or so wavelengths long, it is often used on multiple bands. Again, city dwellers need not apply!

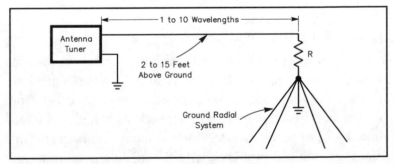

Fig 3-34—The Beverage is an interesting receiving antenna. See the Resources Guide for the dimensions and value of R. These antennas are usually mounted very low—perhaps 5 to 15 feet from the ground.

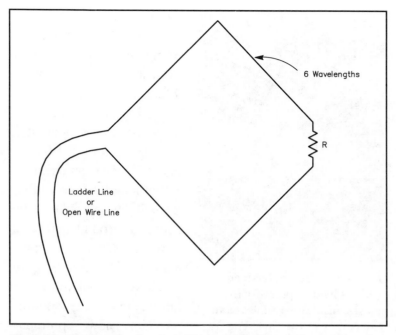

Fig 3-35—Each side of a rhombic is at least several wavelengths long. It is used for both transmitting and receiving.

Mobile Antennas—More Choices for Your Car

Down the road you go. Rig tucked next to your seat, mike in your hand, and whip antenna bent in the breeze as you do the speed limit, talking to Joe several thousand miles away. The classic picture of a mobile installation (Fig 3-36) is a whip antenna with a *loading coil*. This one is mounted on the rear panel of a station wagon. Where are you going to mount your antenna?

You want to place any antenna as high and clear of obstructions as possible. But if you mount your whip on the roof of your car, be prepared to start bumping into things. Many roads and most garages only provide clearance for

Fig 3-36—This center-loaded whip is held in place by the plastic insulator connected to the corner of the roof. The extra support keeps the antenna from swinging out toward the horizontal at high speed.

automobiles, and 10 feet or less is not uncommon. Some parking garages are even shorter—8½ or maybe 9 feet.

That is why many HF antennas are mounted on the side, or even on the bumper of the car. The approximately 8-foot length of the whip allows its base to be 2 feet above the ground, before you have exceeded the magic number of 10 feet.

Every problem has a solution, and many solutions provide new problems. Mounting an antenna close to the car body means under certain turns and accelerations the antenna may swing over and hit the car body, which is not good for the car, antenna or our signal. Therefore, many hams add a plastic standoff from the corner of the roof to the whip. Others simply add a plastic bumper ring to the antenna. If you are concerned about the antenna bending too far back—notice the spring on the base—as you speed down the road, tie an elastic cord (a *bungie cord*) between the antenna and the roof corner or a roof rack.

Where Does the Loading Coil Go?

The loading coil acts just as the coil described previously in the section on shortened dipoles. It substitutes for missing wire. For example, on 40 meters a ¼-wavelength vertical is about 32 feet long. Mobile whips are 8 feet long. The loading coil lets the whip look like it is 32 feet long by substituting (electrically) for the missing 24 feet of wire. One question often asked about mobile antennas is "where does the loading coil go?" The answer, usually, is the middle of the whip. It is possible to put it at the top, bottom, or anywhere in between, but most tests have shown slightly better performance with a *center-loaded* whip antenna.

At least one manufacturer offers a spider-like connector, to be fastened to the lower part of the whip. The spider allows several top sections, with individual loading coils, to be in place simultaneously. This is not very much different from the dipole idea shown earlier, where one feed line is connected to several dipoles. Both allow common feed for several bands. It really means you do not have to stop, unscrew the coil and top section, screw on new ones, and get back in the car when you change bands!

There is one other approach, used by the military. No loading coil. A high-efficiency antenna tuner is mounted directly on the bumper, and an 8-foot whip end-fed, just as a random length wire would be end-fed from your home shack. Adjustment of the tuner is critical, but so is the adjustment of the length of the whip with a conventional loading coil. In both cases, assuming a high-efficiency tuner and high-efficiency loading coils, you must retune every time you change your transmitter frequency by 10 kHz on 80 or 40. You do have a little more room to change frequency without retuning on the higher HF bands.

Efficiency and Grounds on a Car

In the section on long wire antennas, you saw how important it is to provide a good ground system. It is even more important when you want to operate HF mobile. A short whip antenna is not very efficient. With a poor ground you have just about thrown yourself out of the game!

Unfortunately, most new cars are not very cooperative. On the older cars the answer used to be the addition of ground straps. The metal to form a ground plane was there, but the various pieces—car frame, body parts, engine and transmission—were not well connected electrically. New cars often use large plastic assemblies, and there is not very much metal. You may have to run ground busses under the car to connect various widespaced metal parts.

Before picking a location for the base of your antenna, make sure that spot is sheet metal. A fiberglass or other plastic body panel will give you both mechanical problems (it may break under stress) and electrical problems (no close ground connection).

You may want to use a small antenna tuner (see Chapter 5). In the past, mobile whips were tuned by sliding the tip section up and down to make the whip longer and shorter. With a tuner you will not have to do that very often.

One sign of a poor ground system is electrical noise pickup. In any HF installation there will be some electrical noise entering the receiver, but with a good ground system it will be minimized. Before you start to add noise filters, wire shielding and other common cures for car electrical noise, check your antenna ground system. You might be in for a surprise.

A Word of Warning

Most cars today have computer-controlled ignition systems, electronic pollution controls and other microcircuit-based systems. Don't be surprised! The first time you transmit from a new mobile installation, do it in your parking spot. Some cars have been known to stall and quit when there is a strong source of RF close by. See the section on this topic in Chapter 7.

Non-Mobile Mobile

Often the idea of a mobile installation is to get you there, and then you can operate from some good mountaintop spot while sitting in the comfort of your car. It's fun, and a lot safer than trying to crack a DX pileup while doing 55 in traffic.

Fig 3-37 will give you one idea. The Yagi and mast break down to short sections, which fit neatly in the van. A simpler approach is the inverted-V antenna (Fig 3-38). You also can use the mast alone as a vertical, and run a set of wires on the ground as the ground plane or counterpoise.

Boats

This is one of my favorites. I just don't know why the fish bite only during the middle of interesting QSOs. Sail-

Fig 3-37—Mobile operation according to NL7TB and NL7VJ. They used this antenna to operate portable VY1—but not while moving.

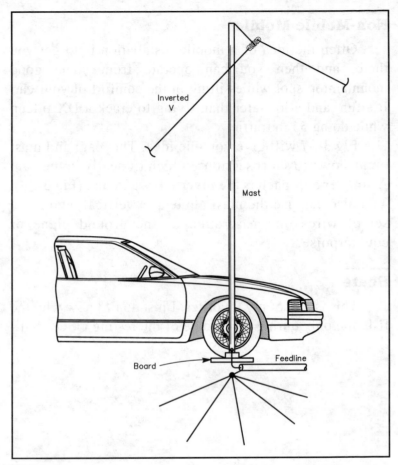

Fig 3-38—A mast can support an inverted V, or with radials it becomes a vertical antenna. The 5-foot sections allow it to be broken down to fit inside the car.

boats are reasonably easy. Either use an insulated stay (Fig 3-39) or run a separate wire to the mast top—either straight up or at an angle.

Power boats often use mobile whips. Whether power or sail, the ground plane is important. Occasionally, a marine or automotive whip will be pictured using the metal

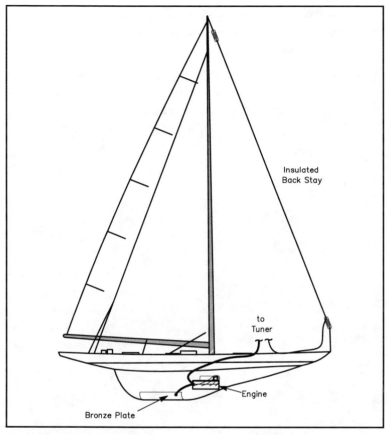

Fig 3-39—Tie the engine (inboard, I/O or large outboard) to the bronze plate. This becomes the grounding system for your radio. Disconnect the antenna from the radio and connect it to the grounding system when thunderstorms threaten.

stern rail as the ground plane. This is usually not a sufficient ground.

One solution consists of wire, and plenty of it! Run several pieces from your antenna tuner ground terminal along the inside of the hull. Tie every large piece of metal to it—your water tanks, engine block, exhaust system and anything else you can reach.

In saltwater, a marine grounding system can help solve the problem. Mount a large bronze plate on the bottom of the hull to make contact with the water. Most marine supply stores carry this plate or some equivalent. Assuming this is your boat, don't use bottom (or any other) paint on the bronze, and clean it each year before putting your boat in the water. A mid-season scrubbing with a wire brush would not hurt, either.

CHAPTER 4

No Pets or Antennas Allowed

My friend Ernie lives in a condo. His name is not really Ernie, and I am not going to give you his call sign. He uses a hidden antenna. His car has call letter license plates, and he does not want to run the risk that one of his neighbors will find out he is operating 40-meter CW from his living room.

Ernie became a ham a few years ago, and did most of his operating on the local 440-MHz repeater from the car. After a few months he upgraded, and with a borrowed receiver and a 15-foot piece of wire lying on the floor started listening to a few of the HF bands.

One evening, at a meeting of the local radio club, he was bemoaning that condo rules kept him from operating on the HF bands. A few of the hams present took up the challenge. Exactly one week later, Ernie was operating on 40 and 20-meter CW with about 50 watts—and no one in his condo knew about it.

If you have a similar problem—or just want to have an inconspicuous antenna—this chapter is for you. Anyone can operate effectively with a dipole at 70 feet or a 125-foot tower. Getting good results with a hidden antenna is a challenge, and it can be fun to meet such a challenge.

After Ernie told us about his problem, we went for a walk around his home. We tried to be inconspicuous (no radio club T-shirts, no hand-held radios and no bright yellow Yaesu radio hats). We then sat down in Ernie's living room with our tools—pencil, paper and a copy of *The ARRL Antenna Book*. The result was a picture that is not printed here, because you can't see a length of #24 wire going out the window and across the lawn to a handy tree. When the sun is just right you can see it, but no one has noticed it in the 12 months it has been in place.

There is no nice, neat way to tell you how to put up an antenna when you are working under zoning, neighborhood, condo or just family restrictions. In this chapter, we will first consider some basic ideas, and then take a look at what other hams have done.

The best way to solve a problem is to make a list of what you know about it. Then you can start to look for solutions. Our first question is, "Why can't you put up a conventional antenna?" Is it local rules—zoning, condo or neighborhood aesthetics?—or are you just limited by space and perhaps finances?

The second question may be more difficult to answer. "Just what is forbidden?" Are all outside antennas banned? How about TV antennas? In a few pages you will see some ideas for making use of TV antennas. Do you have any room for an antenna? How about a balcony? An attic?

Finally what sort of operation do you plan? HF, VHF or UHF? Repeaters? VHF and UHF antennas are much smaller and easier to hide than HF antennas. In Chapter 2, we discuss a J-pole antenna you can tack to a wall and make almost invisible.

Over the years, hams have used many tricks to

camouflage, hide or disguise their antennas. You can use very thin wire for HF long wires. Coaxial feed lines can be covered, painted, run in garden or sprinkler hose or even through drain pipe. Flagpoles are a favorite cover, when appropriate to the surroundings.

Other antennas can be made of aluminum foil, and buried under carpet or even behind wallpaper. A little imagination can lead you to painting antennas and feed lines to match tree bark, brick chimneys and house siding.

One of my first indoor antennas was a center-fed 10-meter dipole. It was mounted just over and behind a picture window curtain rod. At the center of the dipole was a coax connector. When I wanted to operate I closed the curtains, unrolled a length of coax from the rig, and connected it to the matching connector on the dipole.

There are disadvantages to many of these antennas. Any antenna close to a structure will have a distorted pattern and a low efficiency—especially when there are conductive items such as steel beams and household wiring close by. An indoor antenna in a steel frame, concrete floor and concrete ceiling building is usually not effective unless you mount it outside the window or right next to the window.

Occasionally there are some real problems. A small amount of RF energy can set off the *pillbox* type of smoke detectors now very common. Sometimes this is due to RF pickup in the ac wiring, and other times direct pickup in the smoke sensor or circuitry. Transmitted powers of over a few watts can place nasty, if not dangerous, voltages on both antennas and any ground wires (sometimes called *counterpoises*) you use. Painful burns can result from contact with these wires.

Always remember safety. Read Chapter 7 of this book. Be extra cautious if you use an antenna mounted in the attic, on a wall or anyplace indoors. You, your family, neighbors and pets may come very close to the radiating elements. For that reason plan to use low power. You may make fewer contacts, but you'll be avoiding safety problems.

The most important consideration is to avoid erecting any antenna that can present a hazard (physical or electrical) to humans, animals and buildings. Safety first!

Artificial Grounds

In Chapter 1 we saw that a dipole has two parts (halves). A ground-plane antenna also has two parts, but the second part is replaced by a conductive area or ground. A long wire antenna has one visible part, but also requires a conductive ground to operate properly. When a good ground is not connected, the amount of power radiated from the antenna is reduced. Often the main difference between the power that comes out of your rig, and the power actually radiated, is power lost in the grounding system. In the worst case this power shows up on the cabinets, enclosures and wires in the shack. It may give you a bit of a burn when you come in contact with any exposed metal.

From time to time a ham will connect a ground wire from the rig to a nearby water pipe, and things will get worse instead of better. The wire is necessary as a safety measure to prevent 60-Hz voltage differences. At RF frequencies, however, the wire may be resonant, and the amount of RF floating around the shack actually increases.

If you remember that often this ground is acting as the "other half" of your antenna, then the idea of putting some kind of antenna tuner between the rig and the water pipe makes sense. These tuners are often called *artificial grounds.* They can be built or bought—MFJ Enterprises (see the Resources Guide at the back of this book) manufactures one that is a simple tuning network with a power meter. Adjust the network so the power meter reads maximum power out, and you are ready to transmit.

What Have Other Hams Done?

You're not alone. From the time the earliest hams or radio experimenters tried to put a piece of wire out of a window, there was someone who came running over and asked, "Just what do you think you are doing?" Fortunately, there have been many hams before you with solutions that worked for them. These solutions, and your imagination, should result in a reasonable antenna for your particular situation.

Windows—Out and Down

Long Wires

They may not be that long and they are not an elegant solution, but a piece of wire, run out of a window, is one of the most common and certainly easiest way to install a hidden antenna. The wire may be dropped down from the window or run horizontally to a nearby tree. In either case it is fed directly by an antenna tuner (see Fig 4-1). The ground shown was discussed in the previous paragraphs. To achieve best radiation, and least RF in the shack, this ground is as important as the antenna wire location itself.

If you do drop the wire out of a window, remember to look out for people and property below. A 3-ounce fishing sinker will hold the wire down, but it could cause considerable damage if it hits someone or something.

Whether dropped straight down or run horizontally, the small gauge wire will be difficult to see. For 100-foot

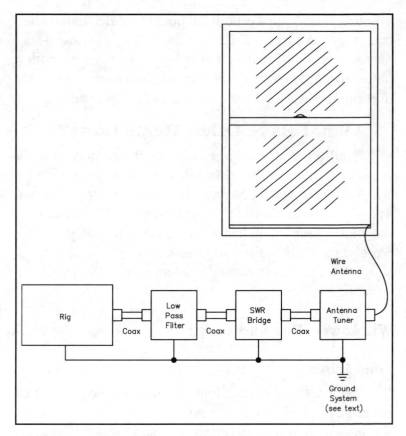

Fig 4-1—Mount the antenna tuner close to the window, and run the antenna wire directly out of the tuner, without any transmission line. See the text for a discussion of the ground system.

runs, #24 or #26 wire will support its own weight, and #28 or #30 is okay for shorter spans.

Most importantly, consider what will happen if it does fall during the night, and someone becomes entangled in it early the next morning! You should choose the lightest gauge that seems to stay up, so if it does fall on the ground it will snap easily.

Table 4-1

Dipole Dimensions for Amateur Bands

Freq MHz	Overall Length	Leg Length
28.4	16' 6"	8' 3"
21.1	22' 2"	11' 1"
18.1	25' 10"	12' 11"
14.1	33' 2"	16' 7"
10.1	46' 4"	23' 2"
7.1	65' 10"	32' 11"
3.6	130' 0"	65' 0"

Table 4-2

Choke Dimensions for RFD Antenna

Freq	RG-213, RG-8	RG-58
3.5	22', 8 turns	20', 6-8 turns
7	22', 10 turns	15', 6 turns
10	12', 10 turns	10', 7 turns
14	10', 4 turns	8', 8 turns
21	8', 6-8 turns	6', 8 turns
28	6', 6-8 turns	4', 6-8 turns

Wind the listed length of coax feed line into a coil and hold in place with electrical tape. The lengths given are not highly critical.

Use the smallest possible pieces of plastic as insulators to reduce their visibility. You can use rubber bands temporarily, but they degenerate quickly in sunlight and temperature extremes.

Take a look at Table 4-1. If your window is higher than the *Overall Length* given in the table for a particular band, then you could use the Resonant Feed-Line Dipole (RFD) shown in Fig 4-2. Since the antenna is coax fed, it is much less sensitive to your ground connections. You do want to

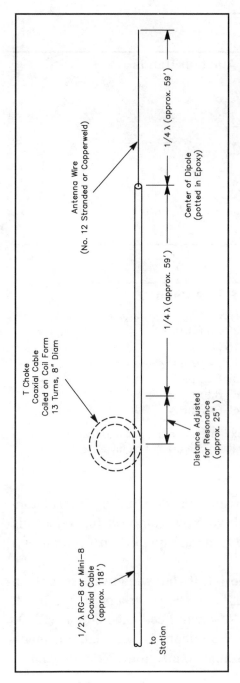

keep the bottom end of the antenna as far from the ground as possible. If your home is in a building that is made of brick or masonry, or has a steel frame, space the entire antenna as far from the building as possible.

The antenna uses a coil known as a *current choke*, made of coax coiled around an 8-inch form. The number of turns, and the amount of coax needed to make this choke, are given in Table 4-2. In some locations the current choke will not be enough to keep RF energy out of the

Fig 4-2—The Resonant Feed-Line Dipole can be dropped out of a window, or hoisted in a tree. Be sure to weatherproof the point where the coax is connected to the antenna wire. The dimensions in the drawing are for 80 meters.

shack. You might try adding a bead balun, such as described in Chapter 5. This antenna can be built quickly, so if you are not sure it will work for you, just drop it from the window and try it!

With a little camouflage this antenna also can be tree mounted. When the coax leaves your shack it can be buried (remember the garden hose trick?) and run to a tree. The end of the wire is hoisted vertically, and the entire antenna runs near the tree. Since it blends into the tree, no one will notice.

Ground-Plane Antennas for Trees and Houses

Chuck Hutchinson, K8CH, described a tree mounted HF ground-plane antenna in *QST* that could be either hung from a tree or "pasted" on a wood-frame building. Once more, construction time is short, and it's easy to build and test.

This simple design is shown in Fig 4-3. Hung from a tree, it is virtually invisible against a background of branches. The coax can be painted to match the foliage or tree bark. If mounted on a wood-frame building, both the antenna elements and the coax can be painted to match the building.

A piece of RG-58 coax runs to the feedpoint of the antenna, and is attached to an insulator. Two radial wires are soldered to the coax-line braid at this point. The radiator is a piece of wire, soldered to the center conductor of the coax. An insulator at the top of the radiator is the support point for the tree-hung configuration.

The dimensions of the radials and radiating element are the *Leg Lengths* in Table 4-1. Plan where the wires will run before deciding to use this idea on your house. If necessary they can be bent—you will lose a little efficiency, but it will still be a good performer.

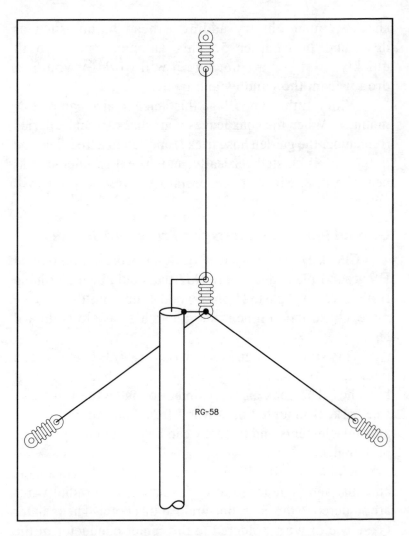

RG-58

Fig 4-3—Dimensions and construction of a wire-element ground plane. Mounted in a tree, or fastened to a wood building, it can be made almost invisible.

Balconies and Mobile Antennas

A favorite place to mount an antenna is a balcony. It has the great advantage of portability—put it up as soon as it gets dark, and take it down in daylight. Use either a resonant mobile whip antenna or your own invention, such as a piece of aluminum tubing mounted on an insulated base (see Fig 4-4). It is a good idea to put the antenna tuner or matching network right next to the end of the radiating element. Clamp the base to the railing, attach the ground system, and you're ready to operate.

A metal railing on the balcony seems to offer an attractive ground for this sort of operation, but unfortunately most such railings do not have enough ground area to be effective. This is a situation where you can use a few radials, perhaps run under the rug in the adjacent room. Keep in mind that in addition to RF safety (see Chapter 7), the antenna and perhaps the radials are exposed. Even at moder-

Fig 4-4—A mobile whip with resonator coils or a length of metal tubing can be mounted on a window sill or balcony railing. The homebrew tuner is located next to the base of the whip or tubing.

ate power levels they can produce RF burns if you, or some-one else (the family dog?), touches them while you are transmitting.

Roofs and Attics Make Good Hiding Places

Gutters, Downspouts and Dipoles

When steel rain gutters started to replace the old wood gutters, you can bet there was some ham who said "Aha—there's my new antenna." Today's aluminum gutters and downspouts let you do the same thing. Run a single wire from your shack out the window, and fasten it to the end of the gutter. As long as the gutter and downspout are supported by dry wood, and the sections are firmly fastened together, you have a perfectly good long-wire antenna.

Make very sure the sections are connected without intervening corrosion, or you may start to generate a great deal of television interference or TVI. If need be, you can isolate sections of the gutter from other sections by inserting thin plastic sheets. These keep the overlapping metal from making contact. Then apply a layer of roofing tar to seal the joint.

Take a look at the longest roof gutter on your home. Is it over 32 feet? If so, by isolating two 16-foot sections you can make it into a horizontal dipole for 20 meters. Again use the *Leg Lengths* of Table 4-1 for each section on the band you want to operate.

TV Antennas are Wonderful

As a ham it was never quite clear to me why some people (and neighborhood associations) would object to beautiful ham antennas, while accepting ungainly and often ugly TV antennas. This lack of understanding never kept me or other hams from taking advantage of TV antennas.

If your operating is primarily VHF and UHF you might

get away with replacing the TV antenna with a small Yagi, and explaining that it is a special single-channel TV antenna. Unfortunately, this can only be a good explanation if your Yagi is horizontally polarized.

You can also try disconnecting the 300-ohm feed line from the TV, and using it with the attached TV antenna and mast. The assembly will act as a random-length wire if you feed it with a tuner, and results in a usable antenna.

TV antennas often require guy wires. Not surprisingly, the one shown in Fig 4-5 required two sets. One set forms an inverted-V antenna for 10 meters, and the other for 15 meters. Table 4-1 gives the wire lengths. You should use

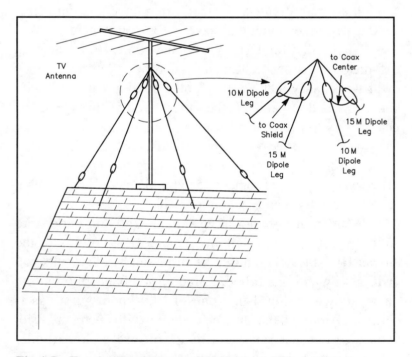

Fig 4-5—Two inverted-V antennas, for two different bands, masquerade as guy wires for the TV antenna. A single coax feed line is used for both inverted Vs. The TV antenna has its own 300-ohm feed line.

copper wire for the guys rather than galvanized guy wire. Now you are not really that surprised that this TV antenna needed two sets of guy wires. A single coax feed line is connected to both inverted-V antennas and taped to the TV mounting mast. Most people would not notice the coax against the mounting mast.

Attics are Great—If You Can Get into Them

Many condos, apartment houses and garden apartments have attics, which make fine hiding places for antennas. As long as the roof overhead is nonconductive (asbestos shakes, wood or ceramic tile), its presence seems to have very little effect on the antenna. Concrete roofs, which are reinforced with steel, often have a major effect and usually mean you will have to look elsewhere.

Many VHF or UHF Yagis, and some 10, 12 or even 15-meter Yagis, can fit. Rotating it may be a problem, but they will work fairly well. You can also build a Yagi with wire elements, and suspend it in the attic. As you might expect, you have to try to keep antennas away from any metal, including ac wiring. The effect of nearby structures on HF Yagis can be severe, and might keep it from providing the gain you want. However, the cost of some wire to build a wire Yagi is small, and you can try it and see for yourself.

Many attics are not large enough, and don't appear to allow you to put in a full size dipole for 20 or any of the lower HF bands. You might be surprised by the results you will get by taking a full size dipole for a band, and folding it as shown in Fig 4-6. None of these configurations is critical. Although the antenna is shown with open wire feed, you also can use coax. As long you use a short (under 50 feet) run of high quality coax, the losses on the lower HF bands will not keep you from getting good results. If you can't fit one of these shapes into your attic, try one of your

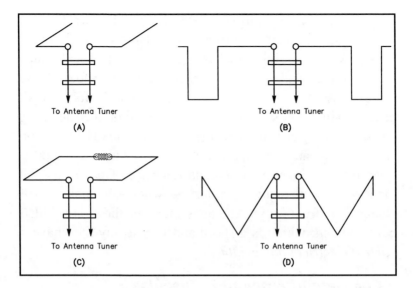

Fig 4-6—A dipole in the attic can be bent in many shapes to fit the space available. Try to keep both sides symmetrical—if possible bend them both the same way.

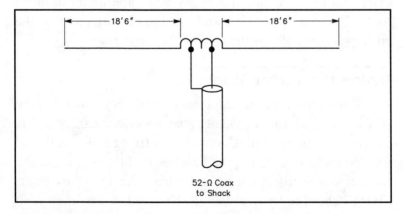

Fig 4-7—The WØSVM "Shorty Forty" center-loaded antenna. The loading coil is made from Miniductor 3029 stock (see Resources Guide in the back of this book). Thirty turns are used, with the center of the coax connected to the center of the coil. The coax shield is fastened to a point one or two turns away. Try both and solder it to the one that gives you the lowest SWR.

own—you might be surprised with how well it works.

A shortened center-fed dipole for 40 meters was designed by WØSVM. The dimensions in Fig 4-7 are not critical. Make it a bit longer, and use fewer turns on the coil. Shorter? Use more turns. If you do not have that almost 40-foot length needed to fit this design, bend the ends. All shortened antennas change their electrical characteristics very rapidly when you change frequency—compared to a full-size half-wave dipole. Therefore, if you use an antenna tuner (see Chapter 5), the tuner will often require readjusting when you make small changes in frequency. Antennas such as these are called *narrow-band*, which is a shorthand way to say they have a *narrow electrical bandwidth*.

A Commercial Antenna in Disguise

There is at least one commercial 2-meter antenna that is a good example of imagination applied to an outside antenna. It consists of a vertical antenna, packaged to look like an extension to the standard sanitary vent pipe found on most roofs. You can further camouflage the unit by painting the coax the same color as the roof surface material.

Inside the Living Room

One of my favorite antennas looked very much like the K8CH's tree mounted ground plane, described earlier in this chapter. It was taped in the corner of a living room wall, and the two radials ran along the baseboard at the bottom of the two adjacent walls. A coax line ran from the rig to the corner. I wish I could tell you about all the rare DX I worked with this antenna, but it wouldn't be true. All it did was put me on 10 meters to talk to the local gang, and it did that very well.

An antenna does not have to be big and obtrusive to do what you want it to. Many of us have made do with a piece of #30 wire taped along three walls of the room and

Fig 4-8—The *MFJ-1786* 10-30 MHz loop antenna is only 3 feet in diameter. *(photo courtesy of MFJ)*

connected to an antenna tuner. It is quick and inexpensive, and when all is favorable works quite well.

Loop Antennas—Commercial and Homebrewed

The MFJ *High-Q Loop Antenna* pictured in Fig 4-8 can be very effective in a living room. It is approximately 3 feet in diameter, and when not in use you can store it in a closet. It is one of several commercial loops available. They are compact, but very narrow-band. If you change frequency you have to retune the loop.

The AEA *IsoLoop* is another good choice. If you look

Fig 4-9—High-Q low-loss components form this AEA IsoLoop. A matching automatic antenna tuner permits you to change frequency without manually retuning the loop. (*photo courtesy of AEA*)

closely at Fig 4-9, you can see it mounted in a shopping cart, on the balcony of an apartment. Wheel it out on the balcony to use, and when you are finished, wheel it back in!

Homebrewed single-turn wire loops are good antennas, if you live in a wood-frame building. The loop can be placed on the floor while operating, suspended from the ceiling or even mounted on a wall. The loop size will depend on the band selected. Fig 4-10 shows the loop and matching network. Each side of the loop is equal to the *Leg Lengths* provided in Table 4-1.

Other Tricks

Take a look out of your window. What's out there? A bird feeder? A picnic table with a beach umbrella? Almost anything already out there, or that could be put out there, can be made into an antenna. A clothesline is almost ideal! In some areas it is not unusual to mount a floodlight in a tree, and run wire to the floodlight. The floodlight can be fake and the wire your antenna. Use your imagination!

We can exhibit our patriotism, and have an invisible antenna at the same time by disguising our antenna in a flagpole. A single wire, placed inside a hollow fiberglass pole, makes a vertical antenna. The ground radials and the

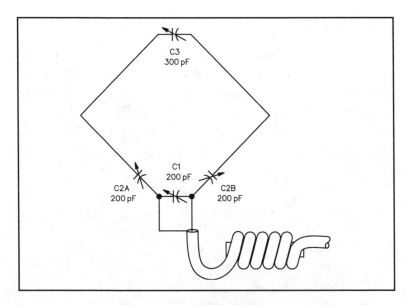

Fig 4-10—A wire loop can be mounted indoors or outdoors if you protect the variable capacitors from the weather. The coil of coax cable is constructed according to Table 4-2 for 40 meters. A loop side length of 28 feet will permit operation on both 30 and 40 meters.

coax feed line are buried out of sight. A metal flagpole also could be used, but then an insulated mounting base would have to be devised for it.

Your car makes a good antenna choice. Parked outside, with a mobile whip, it can be connected to your rig with an inconspicuous length of coax. When you are finished operating, disconnect the coax, roll it up and store it in the car trunk.

Still another option is the wooden flagpole. The antenna is a piece of wire, stapled to the outside of the pole, and then both pole and wire are painted. Fig 4-11 shows a hidden four-band antenna, covering 7, 14, 21 and 28 MHz. See the Resources Guide for the location of construction information.

It's Your Choice

Hidden or disguised antennas can work amazingly well. Many hams use them because they have to. Still others use them by choice, to demonstrate they can meet the challenge of getting good results without erecting a huge tower. One thing is certain—put up one of these unusual antennas, and you will never lack a good topic for an on-the-air discussion!

Fig 4-11—The flagpole is a 7, 14, 21 and 28-MHz vertical antenna in disguise. It is designed to work with 50-ohm coax. By burying the coax and radials, there is no outward sign that this is an antenna.

CHAPTER 5

Feed Lines and Connections Make a Big Difference

I was a ham for many years before I discovered a fundamental truth: Most of what you read and hear about feed lines does not contribute to a better signal. Yes, it is possible to lose a large amount of power in a feed line. This affects both the strength of your signal at the other end, as well as the strength of signals entering your receiver. But, judging from what I've heard on the air, most hams seem to be trying to improve their signal by reducing their *standing wave ratio*—SWR—from 2:1 to 1.2:1, or thereabouts. In 99% of the cases, whether you operate on HF, VHF or UHF, this does nothing for signal strength!

The loudness of a signal or its strength is measured in *decibels* (abbreviated dB). There are two things to keep in mind when using dB. First, the human ear can just about detect a change in strength between 1 and 2 dB. Therefore, if you are listening to a signal that changes power by 1 or 2 dB, you might just notice it—or you might not!

The second thing to keep in mind is the way hams give signal reports. Table 5-1 is the standard table. We are interested in the signal strength or S value, which ranges

Table 5-1

The RST System

READABILITY

1—Unreadable
2—Barely readable, occasional words distinguishable
3—Readable with considerable difficulty
4—Readable with practically no difficulty
5—Perfectly readable

SIGNAL STRENGTH

1—Faint signals, barely perceptible
2—Very weak signals
3—Weak signals
4—Fair signals
5—Fairly good signals
6—Good signals
7—Moderately strong signals
8—Strong signals
9—Extremely strong signals

TONE

1—Sixty-cycle ac or less, very rough and broad
2—Very rough ac, very harsh and broad
3—Rough ac tone, rectified but not filtered
4—Rough note, some trace of filtering
5—Filtered rectified ac but strongly ripple modulated
6—Filtered tone, definite trace of ripple modulation
7—Near pure tone, trace of ripple modulation
8—Near perfect tone, slight trace of modulation
9—Perfect tone, no trace of ripple or modulation of any kind

from 1 to 9. Each S unit is a power *change* of 4. Suppose a ham on the other end gave you a report of S6—*Good signals* according to the table. If you reduced your power by a factor of 4—from 100 watts down to 25 watts—your signal-strength report would go down only 1 S unit to S5 or *Fairly good signals.*

To summarize: To reduce your signal by 1 S unit, you would have to lose ³/₄ of your output power, or 75 out of your 100 watts. Therefore, when we talk about losses due to SWR in the feed line, remember how high these losses would have to be to reduce your signal by just 1 S unit.

In this chapter we are going to take a look at your feed line and the equipment surrounding it. First we will examine the equipment in the shack, from the antenna connector on your rig, up to the feed line going outside. After that we will look at some types of feed lines, and finally the connection between the feed line and the antenna itself. Before we delve into how antennas connect to the equipment in your shack, let's take a look at those three magic letters that seem to keep so many hams occupied—**SWR**.

What Your S Meter Really Tells You

While it is true, in theory, that a difference of 1 S unit is a difference of 6 dB, it's also true that not all manufacturers pay strict attention to this definition. Often, the meter scale is designed for looks, not for accuracy. In addition, the voltage measured by the meter is designed to keep the receiver operating properly, rather than to provide an accurate meter reading. Some rigs come with LED bar graphs in place of a meter, with only 10 elements. This means the entire range of received signals is divided into 10 parts, and these parts have nothing to do with S units.

As Roy Lewallen, W7EL, has pointed out, the calibration of the S meter not only varies from rig to rig, but also varies from band to band on the same rig. The net result is you cannot trust your S meter to measure signals and estimate losses accurately. However, whether a drop of 1 S unit is actually 6 dB, 5 dB or even 4 dB—generally you still have to lose more than 50% of your power to drop a single S unit at the receiving end!

The Mystique of SWR

If you do not want to read a few paragraphs on SWR, I really don't blame you. Just read the following sentence, and you can skip to the next section:

The world does not end if your SWR is as high as 2:1 or 3:1.

To some, SWR is an obsession. To others, it's merely a popular topic of conversation. This is due in part to the ready availability of *SWR meters* or *SWR bridges*. Connected in series with a transmission line, they can provide a feel for "How goes it?" by giving a measure of relative power. But an SWR meter does not tell the whole story.

One company has been selling an antenna matching unit to be mounted in place of the center insulator of an HF dipole. It consists of a (hidden) resistor. The SWR measured on a feed line connected to this unit is very low. You have now achieved the dream of some hams—a very low SWR. The problem with giving in to this obsession is that your power is going into the resistor, rather than into the antenna, where it can do you some good.

There are only three reasons to be concerned about SWR. The first is due to the design of the solid state amplifiers found in some ham equipment. These amplifiers are equipped to limit the output power when the amplifier detects a high SWR. A high SWR in this case means the amplifier was designed to feed a particular load, and is not seeing that load. Therefore, the amplifier is not operating at its design point and may overheat. A *power foldback circuit* is used to reduce the output power, so the amplifier does not fry itself.

The second reason you could be concerned about SWR is if you are using a long transmission line, poor quality line or a type of line that has a high loss on the band you use. We'll look at this in more detail later in this chapter.

Finally, if you are trying to use the wrong transmitter and antenna accessories—such as a low-power antenna tuner on a high-power transmitter—a high SWR can cause arcing in the antenna tuner. Common sense dictates that a tuner rated at 100 watts is not a good choice for a transmitter and amplifier delivering 1500 watts. The same can be said of trying to use a 20-meter dipole with coax feed line on 160 meters. The resultant high SWR may result in arcing and very high losses in the transmission line. If you try hard enough, you could manage to lose a few S units in the transmission line.

In the Shack—The Rig Connection

As demonstrated in Fig 5-1, there can be a great deal of equipment between your rig and the feed line. A low-pass filter is often the first element your transmitted power encounters as it travels out of your rig. This is usually followed by an SWR bridge to give you an idea of what is going on in this line.

Many HF stations include an antenna tuner as the next unit. A switch for selecting antennas may be included in the antenna tuner or added externally. One switch position connects the antenna to a *dummy load*. This is often used to test transmitters without radiating and causing unnecessary interference. The lower half of the drawing shows the tuner feeding a device called a *balun*. A balun provides a convenient way to connect the tuner to antennas that use open wire or ladder line feed lines.

Antenna Tuners

You need not know complex math and transmission line theory to decide if you need an antenna tuner. You do

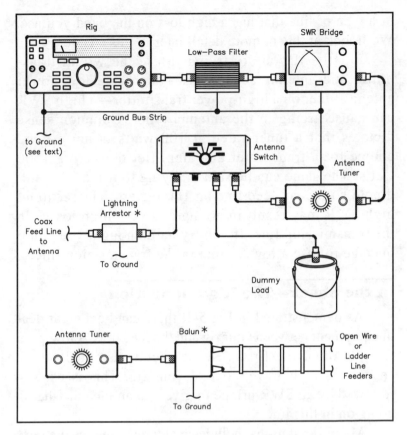

Fig 5-1—The output of your rig may go through a few other devices before it finally gets to the feed line. In the upper drawing the lightning arrestor should be mounted outside the shack, and be connected to a good grounding system. The balun in the lower drawing should also be outside, and a lightning arrestor (Fig 5-11) used.

have to decide what to call it, however. A few of the names you'll hear are *antenna matching unit, antenna tuner, Transmatch* or just plain *tuner.*

The sidebar sums up the story of antenna tuners (the name I prefer).

When to Worry about SWR— and When Not to

☺ *Don't worry* if you are feeding an HF antenna with 50-ohm coaxial cable and the SWR is 3:1 or less. If the length of your feed line is within reason (100 feet or less), the difference between an SWR of 3:1 and 1:1 isn't worth your trouble. You can even run as high as 5:1 SWR with good quality coax and suffer relatively little loss. If your radio is cutting back its output because of an elevated SWR, use an antenna tuner to provide the 50-ohm impedance it needs.

If you are running over 500 watts output, achieving a lower SWR may be in your best interest. Feed line, filter or antenna tuner damage due to arcing may result if you try to run too much power with an elevated SWR.

☺ *Don't worry* if you're feeding an HF antenna with open-wire line and an antenna tuner. SWR has little meaning on the open-wire line until you start talking about SWRs in the range of several *thousand* to one. Simply adjust your tuner for a 1:1 match at your radio and enjoy yourself.

☹ *Worry* if you are operating at VHF or UHF and the SWR is higher than 2:1 at the antenna. Even high-quality coax has substantial loss at these frequencies when the SWR starts creeping up. Adjust the **antenna** to bring it down to something less than 2:1. **DO NOT** use a so-called VHF/UHF antenna tuner in the shack! The tuner will provide a 1:1 SWR for your radio, but you are still living in a fool's paradise. The SWR is still unacceptable on the *antenna side* of the tuner, and that is where you are losing power.

☹ *Worry* if the SWR on your antenna system changes substantially (up or down) for no apparent reason. Some fluctuation is normal, such as when ice coats open-wire lines, but big changes are a warning. Your antenna system may have a problem and you'd better check it out.—*Steve Ford, WB8IMY*

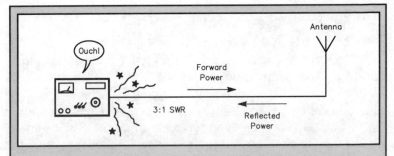

Fig A—Most rigs are designed to connect to an antenna system impedance of 50 ohms. If the rig sees something other than this value, a *mismatch* occurs. *Standing waves* are created in the line, and high RF voltages and currents can develop. When the *standing-wave ratio* or *SWR* becomes higher than 3:1, your rig may put out less power or even be damaged!

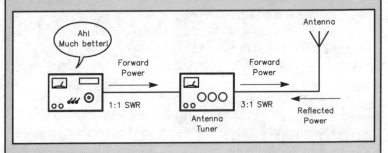

Fig B—By using an antenna tuner your rig "sees" the 50-ohm impedance it was designed for. The higher SWR still exists, but it is on the far side of the tuner and your rig does not see it.

Use an Antenna Tuner If . . .

- *You want to feed your antenna with open-wire line or ladder line.* You will also need a balun connected as shown in the lower part of Fig 5-1.
- *You want to operate your antenna on bands other than those it was designed for.* You could use a coax-

fed 40-meter dipole on 10 meters, for example. An antenna tuner will make your transmitter happy, but remember: On the far side of the antenna tuner the SWR will still be high, and a long length of coax could have undesirable losses. Assuming you are not running power higher than the antenna tuner can handle, you could get away with this arrangement. Keep in mind that you have to lose a great deal of power to reduce your signal on the far end by only 1 S unit.

- *Your antenna is very narrow band*, such as a mobile whip mounted on a car or a short vertical stuck out on a condo balcony railing. Then, rather than adjust the length of the whip or vertical when you change frequency, you can just readjust the antenna tuner.
- *You plan to use an antenna that requires an antenna tuner*, such as an end-fed long wire. Today's transmitters do not respond favorably when you stick the end of a random length wire antenna directly to the center pin of the coax antenna connector on their rear panel!

Don't Bother with an Antenna Tuner If . . .

- *Your SWR is fairly low* on the frequencies you use with the antennas you use on these frequencies. If your transmission line is 100 feet or less, and you are using good quality coax, an SWR of 3:1 should not be a problem on the HF bands.
- *You operate at VHF or UHF.* Antenna tuners are available for these frequencies, but I suggest you save your money. The tuner makes the line look okay to the transmitter, but a high SWR still exists between the tuner and the antenna. Therefore, you will have significant losses in the transmission line—notice the word *will*—and the real cure is to adjust the antenna, so the SWR measured at the input connection to the antenna is low.

- *You have a problem with* television *interference* (TVI) or interference to other household electronics. Most antenna tuners built today are not designed to help (but they won't hurt).

What You Should Look for in an Antenna Tuner

First, buy the highest power rated unit you can manage. Perhaps you are running low power now, but who can tell about next year. In addition, the high-power units can stand the effects of higher SWR. A 100-watt unit may be fine for your 100-watt station when the SWR on its output side is 3:1. If you try to use your 80-meter coax-fed dipole as a "T" shaped antenna on 160, however, the SWR may go to 10:1 or higher. You could have several thousand volts in the tuner. Under these conditions, it will arc—and could fry itself!

Most tuners, such as the 300-watt unit in Fig 5-2, have three controls. Two of the front panel knobs commonly control capacitors at the input and output of the tuner and the third an inductor. The unit shown has a built-in combination SWR meter and wattmeter.

Fig 5-2—This small antenna tuner is made by MFJ. It can be mounted in an auto for mobile HF operation or in the shack for a fixed station. It includes a *cross-needle* SWR meter and power meter. You can read both power and SWR simultaneously with this cross-needle approach. *(Photo courtesy of MFJ)*

You Still Need a Good Ground

A good ground system is a necessary part of the antenna tuner story. For safety, TVI, performance and other reasons, you want to run the heaviest braid you can manage from your rig to all the units in Fig 5-1, and then to a ground point. Lightning arrestors and baluns should be mounted outside the shack and run to a separate outside ground point. The Safety chapter has more information.

Test Instruments

First there was the flashlight bulb. At the time (1930s) it was called a *miniature incandescent bulb,* and it was used to test antennas and transmission lines. In those days, most transmission lines were home-built open-wire lines. SWR was real—instead of just a number you could actually see it! Perhaps you can find a copy of an old radio handbook (pre-1950s) or even an old-timer who can show you *Lecher Wires.* Not only could you see the standing waves on the line, but you could measure wavelength with a ruler.

When coax cable became popular, bulbs (now progressed to neon bulbs) were replaced by various *SWR bridges* or *SWR meters.* The inexpensive ones are not very accurate, but well worth using since they can give you an idea of what is going on in your antenna system. A high SWR simply tells you something is not quite correct—the antenna could be mismatched to the feed line, the feed line broken or saturated with water—or that your antenna is lying on the ground!

The SWR meter mounted in your shack only tells you the story as seen from the shack end of the feed line. Feed lines can act as *transformers*—a short circuit at the antenna end of the transmission line can be transformed into an apparent open circuit at the shack end (if the feed line length and characteristics are particular values). Therefore, the

SWR meter is valuable in monitoring changes in your antenna system, and allowing you to peek at your antenna system. But you have to remember it is only a peek, and through tinted glasses.

Inexpensive SWR meters are not well calibrated. A reading of 3:1 could easily be 2:1 or 5:1. One way to make a quick check on your meter is to reverse the connections. Then follow the directions for measuring SWR, but translate every instruction that refers to *forward* power or reading to *reverse* power or reading. The meter should give you the same SWR whether used in its normal mode or reversed. This test will not allow you to check the absolute accuracy, but you can get a feel for the balance. If the two readings differ, you know not to trust that SWR meter.

A second common and relatively inexpensive test instrument is the *noise bridge,* such as the Palomar unit in Fig 5-3. The bridge contains an extremely low-power

Fig 5-3—A noise bridge is an extremely low-power transmitter that generates a broadband noise signal. By listening to your receiver you can determine antenna resonance, and make other measurements. DO NOT turn your transmitter on when using any noise bridge. *(Photo courtesy of Palomar)*

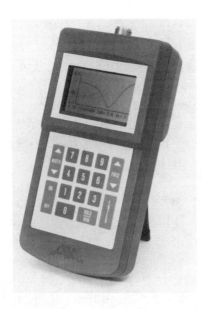

Fig 5-4—An *antenna analyzer* makes a complete set of antenna and feed line measurements. Although slightly more complicated than a noise bridge, it can tell you quite a bit more. You really have to read the instructions before using it. *(Photo courtesy of AEA)*

broadband transmitter called a noise source. It is used with your transmitter turned off. When you follow the directions, it will tell you the impedance of your antenna as seen at the shack end of the transmission line.

In addition to its use as a general test instrument, its primary value in the shack is to tell you the actual impedance seen at this end of the transmission line. Thus, you can tell what sort of adjustment you must make to bring this impedance to the 50 ohms most transmitters were designed to see.

The *antenna analyzer* in Fig 5-4 is a relative newcomer to the ham scene. It is used to provide direct reading and measurements of antennas, feed lines and matching networks. Although it seems relatively complicated, a few minutes of use (following its instructions) can tell you precisely what your problem is— and therefore how to fix it.

Field strength meters have been another popular ham test instrument for many years. They consist of a short antenna and a simple diode receiver or detector. The detector output is connected to a meter that measures your signal strength at the meter location. Unfortunately, when used close to the antenna, especially at VHF and UHF, field strength meters can disturb the pattern. Their calibration is often not accurate, and an increase in the field strength of a transmitted signal does not always mean the meter will read a new value, proportional to the increase in field strength. Therefore, attempts to measure the antenna pattern may lead to bad conclusions. Few field strength meters are sensitive enough to be used at long distances from an antenna.

At HF, the pattern as seen anywhere near the antenna (within a hundred feet) has very little to do with the antenna pattern as the RF launches into the sky. Therefore field strength meters can serve only to tell you if you are transmitting, and allow you to notice any changes that might mean you are developing a problem. Normally the field strength of a fixed antenna remains pretty constant, except perhaps in bad weather. Therefore, changes mean something is changing—and Murphy's Law says these changes are usually in the wrong direction.

Switches and Accessories

Both a balun and a switch are shown in Fig 5-1. Sometimes one or both of these are built into the antenna tuner, and other times external units must be used. Figs 5-5 and 5-6 show compact units designed to be used inside a shack. The switch was designed to mount flat against a wall, and allows the selection of one of four antennas. You can build one of these units yourself, but you must use a switch capable of handling the power of your transmitter. Leads inside the enclosure have to be kept short, and you should never change switch positions while transmitting.

Often you want to make measurements on your rig

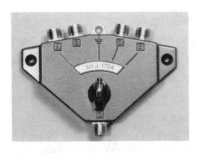

Fig 5-5—In most cases you cannot connect balanced transmission line directly to your rig. This balun is designed to be mounted in a protected area, such as in an enclosure or under a roof overhang. A coax feed line connects it to the antenna tuner, and the balanced transmission line is connected to the other side. This unit has a *ratio* of 4:1—thus 75-ohm coax in the input is matched to 4 times 75 or 300 ohms on the other side. *(Photo courtesy of MFJ)*

Fig 5-6—If you connect your rig to the bottom connector of this MFJ switch you can select one of four antennas from the top connectors. In addition a center grounding position helps protect your rig when it is not in use. *(Photo courtesy of MFJ)*

Fig 5-7—This dummy load can accept full legal power for long enough to run most transmitter checks. It consists of a load resistor immersed in cooling oil. *(Photo courtesy of MFJ)*

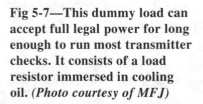

while transmitting full power. If you do so while connected to an antenna, you are violating FCC regulations, as well as being discourteous to other hams who may want to use the frequency you have selected. For these times a *dummy load* such as the one shown in Fig 5-7 is very useful. It consists of a resistor that looks like an ideal 50-ohm load. The resistor is immersed in cooling oil, which is the reason the assembly looks like a large paint can. At low powers, simple resistors without the cooling oil may be used.

Bringing the Feed Line into the Shack

Now you have your rig in the shack and an antenna high in the air. Somehow you have to connect the antenna feed line to the equipment in the shack. Here is an area that is not very technical, but can be a great deal of fun as you exercise your ingenuity.

One approach is the use of *stuffing tubes*. This is similar to the technique used on some ships. First cut a 3 or 4-inch diameter pipe to a length slightly longer than the thickness of your wall. Then cut a matching hole in the wall and insert the pipe. Feed all your coax lines through the pipe. Finally *stuff* the pipe with insect-proof insulation, such as fiberglass. Want to add another transmission line? Simply remove the fiberglass, run the new coax through the pipe, and then re-stuff it with the insulation.

Fig 5-8 is a cross-section view of the installation. The pipe is connected in this sketch to a second piece of pipe (a 90° elbow) pointing down. The single feed line shown has a *drip loop*. Any rain water drips off the loop and does not enter the pipe.

A second approach is shown in Fig 5-9. Here coax, open-wire line or a single wire antenna is sent though a panel. This

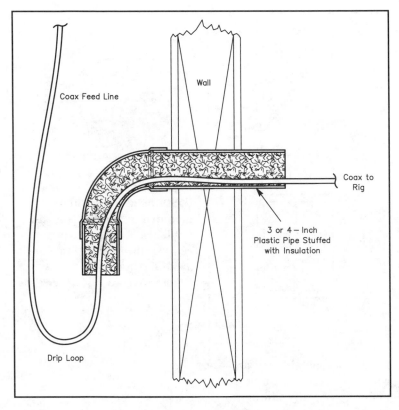

Coax Feed Line

Wall

Coax to Rig

3 or 4 – Inch
Plastic Pipe Stuffed
with Insulation

Drip Loop

Fig 5-8—Neither insects nor rain can get into your shack when you use this version of a ship's *stuffing tube*. When you want to add more antennas take out the stuffing, run the new feed line through, and replace the stuffing.

is also where lighting arrestors such as those shown in Figs 5-10 and 5-11 are mounted. A good ground, usually in the form of an 8-foot ground rod, must be used for the arrestors to be effective. Drive the ground rod into the ground just below the window. But remember, a good ground alone is not complete protection from lightning. Chapter 7 is the place to start reading about lightning protection. The Resources Guide suggests other sources of information.

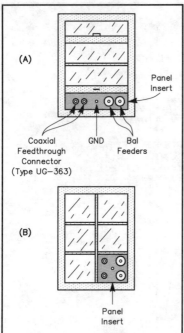

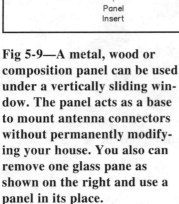

Fig 5-9—A metal, wood or composition panel can be used under a vertically sliding window. The panel acts as a base to mount antenna connectors without permanently modifying your house. You also can remove one glass pane as shown on the right and use a panel in its place.

Fig 5-10—This Cushcraft lightning arrestor should be mounted in a protective case outdoors. Remember to connect the terminal to a good ground (Chapter 7, Safety). *(Photo courtesy of Cushcraft)*

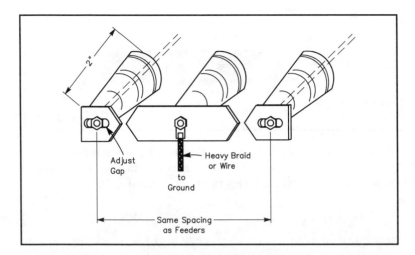

Fig 5-11—A very simple but effective lightning arrestor for open-wire line can be made from three stand-off insulators and a few scraps of metal. Space the outside insulators to match the transmission line spacing.

In the Middle—the Transmission Line

No matter how you say it—"TANSTAAFL" (There ain't no such thing as a free lunch), "You don't get something for nothing" or "You get what you pay for"—this principle holds for transmission lines. If it looks too good to be true it probably isn't. For example, a number of hams have used a single horizontal wire antenna *fed* by another (vertical) single wire. They insisted on calling the vertical wire the *transmission line*. It is certainly a line but not a transmission line. Both pieces of wire formed an antenna, and whether this arrangement worked better than the horizontal wire fed with a more conventional transmission line remains a question.

Other hams have bought "bargain" coax from a national retail distributor. Although, they paid 50% less than the usual brand name products, they found, much to

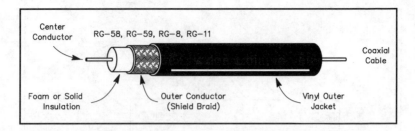

Fig 5-12—*Coax* is short for *coaxial cable*. The name is taken from the construction that has the center conductor, insulation, shield and outer cover all with the same central axis.

their chagrin, that losses were very high. A quick dissection of the coax showed the distributor was able to offer the coax at a bargain price because the outer conductor or shield braid (Fig 5-12) was very sparse. Instead of totally covering the inner insulation the shield looked more like a transparent gauze decoration.

To get RF energy from your transmitter to an antenna you use *transmission line*. A transmission line is a special cable or arrangement of wires. It is commonly called *feed line*, or *feeders* for short. They feed power to the antenna, or feed a received signal from the antenna to the receiver.

Characteristic Impedance

One electrical property of a feed line is its *characteristic impedance*. The spacing between line conductors, their diameter and the type of insulating material determine the characteristic impedance. Characteristic impedance is stated in *ohms*, but these ohms cannot be measured by a simple ohmmeter. You will see stated values from 50 to 600 ohms. The value is often rounded off: 50 ohms is for most purposes the same as 52 ohms, and 70 ohms is the same as 72 or 73 ohms.

Losses, S Units and dB

You are going to hear a great deal about transmission line losses. Most of the time people will be throwing around numbers such as 0.25 dB per 100 feet at 30 MHz. This is the customary way to talk about these losses. There are actually two numbers involved. The first, such as 0.25 dB per 100 feet, means the transmission line loses 0.25 or ¼ dB for each 100 feet of length at the frequency stated—in this case at 30 MHz. This is called the *matched-line loss*, because the load resistance equals the line's characteristic impedance.

There is also an additional loss that varies with SWR. The higher the SWR the higher this loss. At the beginning of this chapter we talked about losses and what they meant in S units. Remember you have to lose ³⁄₄ of your power to lose 1 S unit.

In the HF bands up to 28 MHz, the loss in most coax feed lines is relatively small. The highest example of loss of interest to us is 100 feet of RG-58 or RG-59. It loses about 2 dB at 28 MHz when the SWR is 1:1. You might—just might—be able to hear this difference. If the SWR is high enough to cause the loss of another 1 dB now you have lost 3 dB— a total of ¹⁄₂ S unit.

Rather than plow though the arithmetic for all of the cases you might encounter, you can just follow the guide rules in the next few sections.

Coaxial Cable

Several different feeder types are available for amateur use. The most common is *coaxial cable*. Called *coax* for short, this feed line has one conductor inside the other. It's like a wire inside a flexible tube. The center conductor is surrounded by insulation, and the insulation is surrounded by a wire braid called the shield. The whole cable is then encased in a tough vinyl

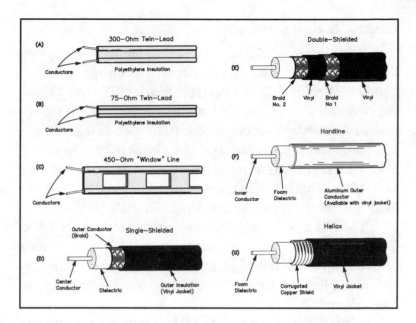

Fig 5-13—These are the most common types of transmission lines. Single shielded coax (D) is the type used by most hams. To ensure the lowest loss VHF or UHF repeaters usually use Hardline (F). Many hams would like to use Hardline for their stations at home but it is difficult to work with and relatively expensive.

outer coating, which makes the cable weatherproof. Coax comes in different sizes, with different electrical properties. Fig 5-13 shows several types of coaxial cables used by amateurs.

The most common types of coax have either a 50 or 72-ohm *characteristic impedance.* Coax designated RG-58, RG-8 and RG-213 are 50-ohm cables. Some coax designations may also include a suffix such as /U, A/U or B/U, or bear the label *polyfoam.* Feed line of this type may be used with most antennas. Cables labeled RG-59 or RG-11 are 72-ohm lines. Many hams use these types to feed dipole antennas.

The impedance of a half-wave dipole far from other objects is about 73 ohms. Practical dipoles placed close to the earth, trees, buildings, and so on, have an input impedance closer to 50 ohms. In any case, the small impedance mismatch caused by using 50 or 72-ohm cable as an antenna feeder is unimportant. Thus, if you have a length of coax and plan to feed a single HF dipole, the selection of 50 or 72-ohm coax will not make much difference.

In choosing the feed line for your installation, you'll have a trade-off between electrical characteristics and physical properties. The RG-58 and RG-59 types of cable are about $^1/_4$ inch in diameter, comparatively lightweight and reasonably flexible. RG-8, RG-213 and RG-11 are about $^1/_2$ inch in diameter, nearly three times heavier and considerably less flexible. RG-8, RG-213 and RG-11 will handle much more power than RG-58 and RG-59.

The larger coax types, RG-8, RG-213 and RG-11, have less signal loss than the smaller types. If your feed line is less than 100 feet long, you won't notice the small additional signal loss, at least on the HF bands. This, combined with light weight and flexibility, is why many HF operators find the smaller coax better suited to their needs. The smaller feed line costs about half as much per foot as the larger types.

On the VHF/UHF bands, however, you will find the losses in RG-58 and RG-59 more noticeable, especially if your feed line is longer than about 50 feet. On these bands, most amateurs use RG-213 coax, or even lower-loss special coaxial cables.

Coaxial cable has several advantages as a feed line. It is readily available, and is resistant to weather. Most common amateur antennas have characteristic impedances of 50 to 70 ohms. Some types of coax are made to be buried in the ground. It can be bent, coiled and run next to metal

It's Coax Decision Time!

Coax is convenient, available and widely used. I am going to feed my new antenna with coax. But which coax? Do I need 50-ohm, 70-ohm or 72-ohm line? Time to decide.

First of all, there is no real difference between 70 and 72-ohm coax. And for most practical antennas, you can use either 50 or 70-ohm line without ever noticing a difference at the receiving end. Therefore, the choice of coax is a matter of performance and cost—as long as you stay with brand names.

The table shows what sort of losses you will get with three selected coax types. RG-58 and RG-8 come with a variety of suffix letters—/U, /F, /AU and others. They are all about the same. Some have a little more loss and some a little less. Some weigh a little more and some a little less. The LMR 400 is typical of the moderately priced, new generation coax. Roughly the same diameter as RG-8, its cost may be 20% or 30% more and its losses 50% less than the older coax types. Other LMR series coaxes cost more and have less loss.

Loss in coax feed line varies with SWR. The table shows the losses on three bands, and for two values of SWR. The numbers are in dB. But before you get all excited about these numbers, keep in mind what a dB means to **you**. Unless you plan to be a world-class contest operator, scratching for every possible competitive advantage, a few dB are not that important. Remember, with a perfectly calibrated S-meter, 6 dB is 1 S unit!

Coax Cable Losses

Loss per 100 feet — for 50 feet divide the loss by 2

Band	SWR = 2:1	SWR = 5:1	Coax Type
80 meters	1.0 dB[1]	1.6 dB	RG-58[2]
10 meters	3.0 dB	4.4 dB	RG-58
2 meters	7.2 dB	8.9 dB	RG-58
440 MHz	DO NOT USE[3]	DO NOT USE	RG-58
80 meters	0.4 dB	0.8 dB	RG-8[4]
10 meters	1.4 dB	2.5 dB	RG-8
2 meters	3.5 dB	5.2 dB	RG-8
440 MHz	DO NOT USE	DO NOT USE	RG-8
80 meters	0.2 dB	0.5 dB	LMR 400
10 meters	0.7 dB	1.3 dB	LMR 400
2 meters	1.7 dB	2.6 dB	LMR 400
440 MHz	2.8 dB	4.3 dB	LMR 400

Notes

[1]Numbers are rounded off and approximate.

[2]RG-58 is 50-ohm cable. RG-59 is 72-ohm cable with losses and characteristics similar to RG-58.

[3]Losses are greater than 10 dB. Pick a better coax, such as one of the LMR series.

[4]When you order RG-8 it is now usually replaced by RG-213, which has similar characteristics.

This table was compiled with information supplied by The Wireman, Inc.

Installing Coax Connectors— Tricks of the Trade

There are almost as many discussions about installing coax connectors as there are discussions about antennas. Hams often find this a difficult job. No one ever says it is easy, but there are little tricks that can make it less frustrating. The Resources Guide contains the dimensions and step-by-step process for mounting the connectors on several different types of coax. Here are a few tricks to keep in mind.

- Use a large soldering iron; at least 100 W and perhaps as much as 300 W. Solder quickly and remove the soldering iron from the work surface as soon as possible.
- Use sharp tiny clippers to cut the braid evenly. Press Jones, N8UG, suggests using cuticle clippers.
- Follow the directions and measure carefully. An extra $1/32$ inch or even $1/64$ inch can make a difference.
- Some hams tin the braid with solder, and then cut it with a rotary tubing cutter such as plumbers use.
- Use good connectors. They do not have to be silver or gold plated, but they do have to be clean. If you bought them loose at a flea market or in bulk from a surplus sale, clean them before trying to solder to them.

Use solder. Don't even consider the "no-solder, push-on" types of connectors sold by some parts retailers. There may be good uses for these connectors, but your transmitter feed line is not one of them!

with little effect. You should always avoid sharp bends when you run coax. A good rule of thumb says you should use at least a 6-inch radius for a 90° bend.

Parallel-Conductor Feed Line

Parallel-conductor feed line is another popular line type

for use below 30 MHz. The most familiar example of this feeder is the 300-ohm ribbon used for TV antennas. It has two parallel conductors encased along the edges of a strip of plastic insulation. We often call this kind of line *twin lead*. Several types of parallel-conductor feed lines are drawn in Fig 5-13.

Low-cost, lightweight TV-type 300-ohm line can be used for low-power transmitters (100 watts or less). Use good quality line to avoid replacing it due to weather.

Open-wire feed line is another type of parallel-conductor line. It contains two wires separated by plastic spacer rods. There is a rod every few inches along the feeder to maintain a uniform wire separation. The primary insulation is air. Often called *ladder line*, this type usually has a characteristic impedance between 450 and 600 ohms. The conductors can be bare wire, or they might be insulated with plastic. Ladder line can handle much higher power than twin lead. The commercial ladder line shown in Fig 5-14

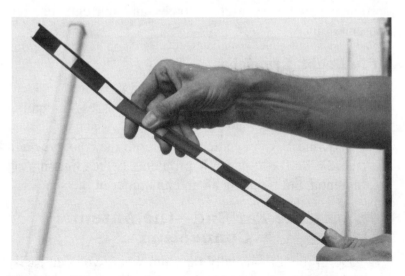

Fig 5-14—*Window* **line is a compromise between 300-ohm TV-line and open-wire line. It usually has less loss than the TV-line but is easier to work with than the open-wire line.**

uses plastic insulation. It looks like standard 300-ohm line in which windows have been cut; thus it often is called *window line*.

Parallel-conductor lines have some disadvantages. For example, they cannot be coiled or run next to metal drain pipes and gutters without adverse effects. Another drawback is their characteristic impedance of 300 ohms or higher. They cannot be connected directly to most transmitters. You will need a balun to connect your transmitter or transceiver to parallel-conductor line. Parallel-conductor lines are not normally used today at VHF/UHF because of these disadvantages.

The major advantage of ladder line is its very low loss. This means you can use this feed line with antennas having high SWRs, without losing appreciable signal due to the SWR. At HF this means you can feed a dipole, cut to one band, with RF at another band without losing very much in the feed line. But be careful—as mentioned before, you may produce some very high voltages and currents in your antenna tuner.

If In Doubt, Remember . . .

- if you use coax, buy good quality coax
- runs of 100 feet or less cause very small losses—assuming the SWR is less than 2:1 or even 3:1
- at VHF and UHF pay attention to both the coax type and the SWR; fix high SWR problems by readjusting the antenna, not by using an antenna tuner in the shack.

At the Far End—the Antenna Connection

Up in the air—usually far from where you can easily reach it—the feed line connects to the antenna. Just because it is usually not readily accessible, you should take a little

If I Had My Way

I would buy an old antenna tuner—one of those battered looking, bulky jobs you often see at flea markets. Inside there would be a large number of wires connecting the front panel switches to large coils, perhaps some jumper wires with clips, and no balun in sight. On the back panel would be two ceramic stand-off insulators, and one ground terminal. Typical of this generation of tuners is the *Johnson KW Match Box.*

Why am I interested in one of these antiques? Certainly not for their beauty, or the large amount of space they occupy. No; it's because they were specifically designed to match a coax line from a transmitter to balanced transmission line—**without a balun**!

Baluns are fine devices, when used in their design applications. This means they were not really meant to be used to convert from unbalanced line to balanced line unless they are attached to their *design impedances.* They work fine when they are connected to 50 ohms on one end and 50 ohms, 300 ohms or 450 ohms on the other—whatever their design was.

I like the idea of using a dipole fed with open-wire line. It is an efficient antenna, good for many bands, and the losses in the feed line are very small. Unfortunately, down at the transmitter end, I have to use a balun to connect the open-wire line to my antenna tuner. Sometimes this is fine. Everything works well, and the balun with its ferrite core stays cool. Other times, on certain bands, some of my output power goes into heating the balun. The oil burner in my house is a much more efficient way to get some heat.

That's why I like the idea of using one of these old tuning units: no balun, and (usually) low loss. If you are interested in building one yourself, the Resources Guide has more information. —*Paul Danzer, N1II*

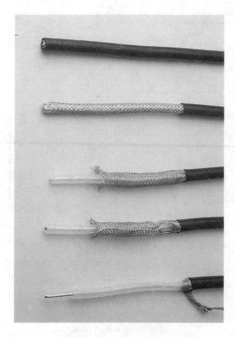

Fig 5-15— Preparing coaxial cable for connection to an antenna. A— Remove the outer insulation with a sharp knife or wire stripper. If you nick the braid, start over. B— Push the braid in accordion fashion against the outer jacket. C—Spread the shield strands at the point where the outer insulation ends. D—Fish the center conductor through the opening in the braid. Now strip the center conductor insulation back far enough to make the connection and tin (flow solder onto) both center conductor and shield. Be careful not to use too much solder, which will make the conductors inflexible. Also be careful not to apply too much heat, or you will melt the insulation. A pair of pliers used as a heat sink will help. The outer jacket removed in step A can be slipped over the braid as an insulator, if necessary. Be sure to slide it onto the braid before soldering the leads to the antenna wires.

extra time, and put in a little extra effort, to make this connection properly and securely. Wind, ice, and rain are only the start. If you live within a few hundred miles of the seacoast, salt spray can play havoc, as can acid rain and ozone in any area.

Follow Fig 5-15 if you are connecting coax directly to a Yagi or a dipole. These steps to split the end of the coax into two conductors are only a start. After connecting the coax to the antenna you must seal the end, and protect all the exposed metal from the elements. Usually one winter in salt spray is enough to induce severe corrosion on any exposed end. One or two heavy rainstorms can also start the process of failure by sending water down *the inside* of the coax, if it is not sealed.

Most flexible plastic/rubber compounds designed for outdoor use are acceptable for sealing the ends, as long as they do not contain a corrosive solvent. Just pick one that remains flexible at low temperatures (read the container). You also can seal the end by wrapping it in a good outdoor tape such as 3M *Super 33+ Vinyl Tape* as the first step. Then seal the entire assembly with 3M *Scotchkote*. Several putty-type compounds are also available. They are normally used over both wires and connectors. Hams have reported mixed results with these products. Some seem to work fine for a period and then start to leak. If you want to try one of these, ask someone locally who has used that exact product.

Some antennas call for the use of baluns at the antenna end of the feed line. One type of balun, often called a *current choke balun*, consists of a coil of coax (Fig 5-16) located at the end of the feed line. Another common balun is used in place of the center insulator (Fig 5-17) of a dipole. It consists of a piece of PVC tubing (containing the balun) with a coax fitting on one end of the tubing and two hook-eyes on the other end. The antenna sections attach to the two hook-eyes, and the coax feed line to the connector on the bottom.

The *bead balun,* also known as a W2DU balun, uses a number of ferrite beads strung over the coax transmission line near the antenna end (Fig 5-18). The photo shows a short section of coax, terminated in a connector at one end and two wire leads at the other. To make one of these baluns for a particular antenna, just slide the ferrite beads over the coax before you either solder a connector or attach the coax

Fig 5-16—An RF choke balun is made by coiling the feed line just below the connection to the antenna. This technique prevents current from flowing on the outside of the feed line, which often occurs when the feed line is not brought away perpendicular to the antenna.

to the antenna. Then tape the beads in place with weatherproof tape.

For RG-58A transmission line (outside diameter 0.195 inch) use 50 Amidon number FB-73-2401 beads. End-to-end these beads will cover about 1 foot of the transmission line, and it makes a compact, neat package when securely taped. For RG-8, which has a 0.405-inch outside diameter, use 12 Amidon FB-77-1024 beads. The 73 and 77 in the part numbers describe the material composition used to make the beads. These two compositions are designed for the HF bands—that is, 160 through 10 meters. For the 2-meter band the bead part number should contain the number 43. See the Resources Guide for more information on obtaining these beads.

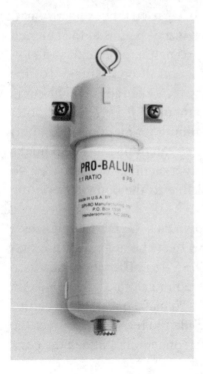

Fig 5-17—The case of this balun also acts as the center insulator for an HF dipole. *(Photo courtesy of Spi-Ro Manufacturing)*

Popular multiband HF antenna designs often require the use of a specific length of a selected feed line type. If you plan to use one of these designs—such as a *G5RV* or a *Carolina Windom*—use the exact feed line type and length specified for the antenna.

Just remember—when it comes to the connection

Fig 5-18—Fifty ferrite beads (such as FB-73-2401) strung over the coax makes a balun. See the Resources Guide for ordering information.

at the top of the antenna—good mechanical construction and weatherproofing will keep the antenna up and working for many years.

CHAPTER 6

Holding Your Antennas in the Air

Notice that the title of this chapter is in the plural—*Antennas*. Many hams plan to put up just one antenna but somehow the number of antennas always increases with time. As you read this chapter, and decide just how you are going to support that new dipole or Yagi, keep in mind that not only will you be making changes to this antenna, you will also be adding additional antennas as time goes on.

At Home

Plan It Out

At this point you should have an idea what bands you want to operate, and just how much money the piggy bank will support for a new antenna. The final piece of the puzzle is to decide where you can put the antenna and how to support it.

Step one is to take a walk. Sure, you know every tree, rock, wire and twig around your home. But did you ever look at it from the point of view of an antenna? Let's suppose you have 70 feet or so between two trees and plan to put up a 40-meter dipole. Each end of the dipole connects through insulators to a piece of guy wire. The guy wire runs over the highest branches you can reach with a fishing rod and a small sinker. But where will the sinker go if you miss? How will your neighbor feel when 3 ounces of lead comes crashing through her window?

If you are lucky enough to have a tower, it may fit beautifully behind the house. But is there enough room to assemble it on the ground and then raise it into position?

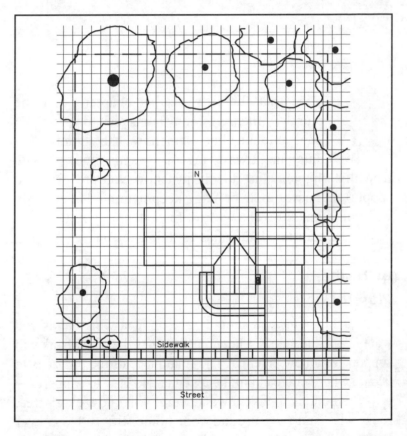

Fig 6-1—Plan your installation using a site map. Include everything that might affect the antenna, including obstacles to erecting it.

Will your guy wires be anywhere near the power lines? So take a walk before you make any final decisions on your new antenna location. Consider each step needed to put up the antenna. Then you will be ready to do the work. A site map (Fig 6-1) is a handy tool for planning your antenna. It doesn't have to be a work of art, but it should include all possible obstacles such as trees and tall shrubs. Draw in the antenna, the guy wires (if any) and the path you intend to follow with the feed line. Street locations, your neighbor's property, power lines and walkways all can make a difference where you put the antenna.

Often you will read a warning: *stay away from power lines!* There are really two parts to this warning. First, stay away from them when erecting your antenna. Second, and no less important, make sure that if your antenna, tower, guy wires or any other part of the antenna system falls they will not make contact with the power lines.

Don't hesitate to use existing structures. The house shown in Fig 6-2 has its roof peak about 30 feet in the air. Mount a length of TV mast at each end, and you have a dipole 35 feet or so in the air. It is a lot easier and cheaper than trying to put up two 35 or 40-foot masts. As long as the roof is essentially a nonconductor such as asphalt shingles or tiles, the antenna does not have to be very far from the roof. Do not try to place a large tension on the mast sections, unless they have a guy wire opposing the pull of the antenna. Often this guy wire will have to be fastened to a tree, pole or other support near the house.

In your planning, remember the law. In this case we are talking about local laws, not FCC regulations. Many towns have a requirement to apply for (and pay a steep fee for) a building permit for structures. Municipalities do have the right and duty to enforce reasonable regulations concerning the safety of life and property.

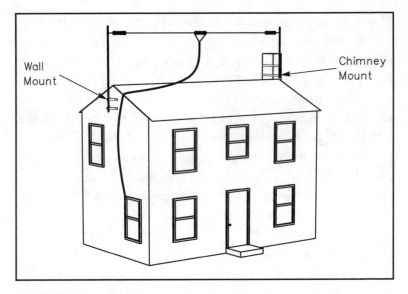

Fig 6-2—Your house can be part of the antenna support. Wall mounts and chimney mounts will hold up one end of a wire antenna, a vertical or a small Yagi.

It pays to work with your neighbors. Discuss your plans with them, listen to their suggestions and introduce them to the positive aspects of ham radio. Nothing will get you through a local zoning or building hearing faster than a few of your neighbors, standing up and saying they support your application.

You may have heard of something called PRB-1. It is a ruling, issued by the FCC, reminding local governments that the Federal government regulates Amateur Radio. It uses words such as "accommodate reasonably" and "minimum practicable regulation." This is usually called a "Federal preemption," and applies to unnecessarily restrictive zoning ordinances and building codes. Even with this federal law, applying for a permit over a neighbor's objection ("it doesn't look nice—it ruins the neighborhood") may result in delays and problems. As many hams have found, PRB-1 can be useful in acquiring the permit. However, there have been cases where the local boards have stalled an application rather than incurring the wrath of many voters. You have only one vote and your massed neighbors have many.

Towns have been known to refuse to issue a permit for a 50-foot high self-standing tower as a violation of fire codes. Their reasoning is they do not have a ladder truck that can fight a major blaze on the top of your tower. When you apply for a permit, you may not always receive what you think is a rational response. If possible, avoid major construction, and don't be surprised if obtaining that permit is not as easy as you might think.

If you think you are going to run into real problems or just need advice, the Resources Guide has further information for you. Your local radio club is another source of help. Most likely one or more of the members have already been through the process in your town or city, and can offer the benefit of their experiences.

Towers, Trees and Poles

It would be a nice world if we could all afford a professionally erected tower, certified to withstand any storm, for our antennas. By the way, it also would have to be attractive enough to win the support and affection of your family members and neighbors! Since this is not the real situation, we usually have to compromise and do the best we can.

Nothing in this discussion should be taken to allow a compromise on safety. Hams have successfully used each of the suggestions made here for many years. But it is possible to make a wrong choice, and cause a potentially dangerous situation.

For example, many hams use 10-foot TV-mast sections for supports. There is at least one national electronics distributor who sells a "lightweight" mast section that has all the strength of the walls of an aluminum soda can. Select this material and you can have problems.

Trees: The Supports Mother Nature Supplies

Trees are a favorite support for the ends of dipoles and other wire antennas. The counterweight technique in Fig 6-3 is a standard way of keeping tension on the antenna wire. If you are going up 20 or so feet in an old oak tree you probably don't need the counterweight. Just tie the line to a cleat

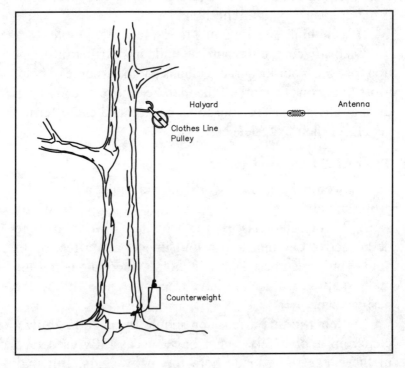

Fig 6-3—The counterweight keeps tension on a wire antenna. The safety wire allows the counterweight to move up and down as the tree sways but keeps the weight from swinging free.

screwed in the tree. If the tree or tree branch you are using will move in the wind, however, the counterweight is a good idea. Neither the counterweight nor the cleat should be accessible to youngsters—especially those who have a Tarzan instinct.

An alternative to the counterweight is the use of springs (Fig 6-4). In any case, both the counterweight and the springs should have safety wires. With this addition, if any part of the antenna breaks neither the springs nor the counterweight will fly off into space.

The pulley system in Fig 6-3 is a good idea if you can get up to screw it into the tree. Often this is impossible.

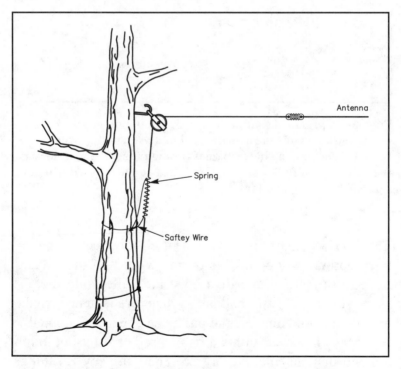

Antenna

Spring

Saftey Wire

Fig 6-4—A spring may be used in place of a counterweight. Thread a safety wire, such as used with garage door springs, through the spring and securely fasten it to the tree.

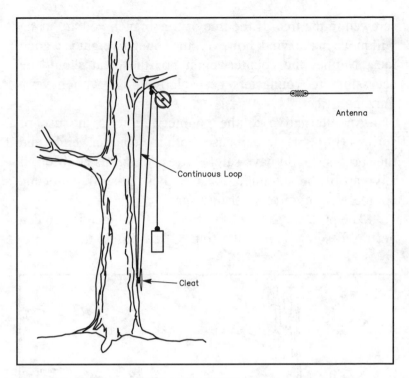

Fig 6-5—A practical solution to the tree climbing problem is a continuous loop of rope or wire used to hoist a pulley over a tree branch. The antenna halyard goes through the pulley. Make sure the halyard and pulley sizes are matched so the halyard will not slip off the pulley and jam.

Then the system of Fig 6-5 can be used. Connect the pulley to a continuous loop of line or guy wire. Run the halyard through the pulley and then hoist the pulley into the air. Make sure the halyard and pulley sizes are matched, so the halyard cannot come off the pulley and become jammed.

Many hams use either a fishing rod or slingshot to run a monofilament line over a tree. There are several things you should recognize before you attempt to place the line where you want it. First, on a warm and windless day, just

Slingshots and Fishing Rods

Chuck Hutchinson, K8CH, combined the advantages of a fishing rod with those of a slingshot to make this unit. A fishing reel, wound with monofilament line, is fastened to the slingshot handle with automotive hose clamps. A 2-ounce sinker is tied to the end of the line, and the sinker shot over the tree. Chuck's device combines the advantages of both a fishing rod (the line goes out in a straight line following the sinker) and a slingshot (the sinker can be shot up almost vertical.)

As with any slingshot—or whenever you are tossing a few ounces of lead in the air—**Safety First!**

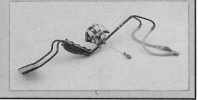

as you make your cast, the only 50 MPH breeze in 200 miles will suddenly materialize just at treetop level. It will carry your sinker at right angles to the point you tried to hit. Next, your neighbor, who has been gone on vacation for the last 6 months in Australia, will suddenly appear and ask what you are doing. Perhaps the best thing you can do in this case is to mutter something about trying to catch a catfish that crawled up the tree trunk. As your neighbor tries to digest your statement, retreat into your home.

After your neighbor leaves, use the monofilament to pull a heavier line such as shipping twine over the tree. The twine is used in turn to pull a length of light rope, and finally the rope to pull the end support line—either guy wire or non-rotting rope—over the tree. As you tie one of these lines to the other use the smallest knots possible. Tape all loose ends, so they are not caught by the tree bark as you pull on the lines.

Any antenna held by a line over a tree branch is likely to become a permanent addition to the tree. At some point after you hoist the antenna, the tree bark may grow around the line. Therefore, you may retain a piece of the antenna in the tree forever, without being able to get it down. One successful approach to keeping the antenna from becoming fixed is to lower the antenna every few months. How to remember this chore, month after month, year after year, is a problem best left to your imagination.

Fig 6-6—Roof-mounted tripod towers range from 3 to 10 feet in height. They are often a very economical alternative to ground-mounted towers. *(Photo courtesy of Jane Wolfert)*

Taking Advantage of your House Height

A handy antenna support is a short rooftop mount such as the one in Fig 6-6. It saves ground space, and picks up the height advantage of the distance from the roof to the ground. Use roofing-tar sealant as shown in Fig 6-7. You must plan to inspect the seal at least once a year.

A 3-foot tripod can support a small HF Yagi or a fairly large VHF or UHF Yagi. If you use a long (10-foot) mast protruding from this tripod, you will want to guy the mast near the top. The tripod will also support a vertical antenna.

Before installing the

mount make sure it is level. Place a short mast section in the tripod, and then use a carpenter's level to see if the mast is vertical on two sides 90° apart. Use ¼-inch lag bolts about 2 inches long to screw the mount to the roof. Plenty of roofing tar applied to the area will ensure water-tightness. Chimney and wall mounts are also handy for small antenna supports. Make sure that the mounting lag screws for a wall mount are fastened into either the house frame ("two-by-fours") or another part of the structure. Just screwing them into the

Fig 6-7—The wood on top of the roof should be matched by supports under the roof when the mounting lag bolts do not hit an interior beam. Use plenty of roofing tar as a sealant and preservative.

siding or the backing board behind the siding is not usually sufficient. With an antenna mounted at the top of a mast, the mast itself will act as a lever, pivoting around the upper wall or chimney mount bracket. Therefore, screw them in securely, and separate the two brackets as much as possible.

Wall mounts have the disadvantage that with time they may rust and stain the house siding. Chimney mounts also have a disadvantage—they may take down the chimney. Normally, chimney mounts fasten with steel straps that go around the chimney. If the chimney looks at all chipped or cracked, pick another type of mount!

Antennas mounted above active chimneys are subject

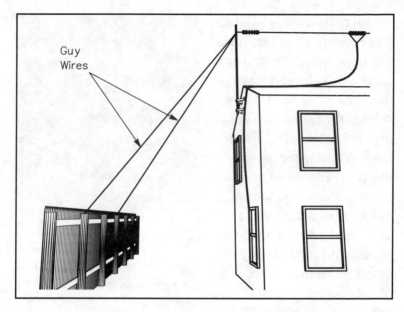

Fig 6-8—Guy wires are often needed. The wall mount shown is pulled in one direction by the end of a dipole and the forces balanced by one or two guys to a nearby fence.

to heat and exhaust particles. Mounting a rotator directly above a chimney is not a good idea.

You will often have to guy a wall or chimney-mounted mast. One of these guy wires will probably have to be fastened off the house structure (Fig 6-8), and on a nearby tree or fence. Therefore, pick the mounting location carefully, so you can fasten this last guy wire.

Every Ham Would Like a Tower

Most hams consider towers the ultimate in antenna supports. There are many tower types, mounting arrangements and heights available.

A crank-up tower, such as the one shown in Fig 6-9, allows you to bring your antenna down to a lower level for installation or maintenance, and as a precaution when very bad storms are forecast. The sections nest or slide within each other. The rotator cable and feed line in the photo are shown very slack because the tower is not fully extended. When the tower is extended to its full height, the cables run neatly, parallel to the tower. Typically, the nested height of this type of tower is a little less than $^1/_3$ the extended height—a 70-foot extended tower would have a 27 or 28-foot nested height.

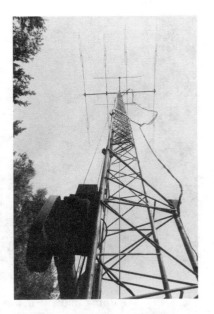

Fig 6-9—This *crank-up* tower is made by Tri-Ex. When it is collapsed or cranked down, the sections nest one inside another. The winch on the left does the actual cranking. Properly installed and maintained, the tower will last for many years. (*Photo courtesy of Tri-Ex*)

One hapless ham had a little accident, and the result is pictured in Fig 6-10. Given the chance, time and weather can destroy an installation. The towers shown in Figs 6-9 and 6-10 are set in a concrete base, but the one in Fig 6-10 was badly damaged by wind. Fortunately, the house itself does not seem to be affected by the tower collapse.

A clever alternative for mounting antennas is the *Hazer* in Fig 6-11. The tower is used as a set of rails and the antenna, rotator and cables literally climb up and down while you stay firmly on the ground.

Some towers are made of tubular steel. The unit in

Fig 6-10—We don't know if it was lack of maintenance or improper installation, but a windstorm reduced this dream tower and antenna installation to a twisted mess. *(Photo courtesy of Ron Blackburn)*

Fig 6-12 has a pivot point about ¼ of the way up. This allows the tower to be tilted over for mounting the antenna and for maintenance.

The tower photographs should remind you to stress safety. If possible, choose a tower arrangement that allows you to work either on the ground or close to it. Avoid climbing if possible. Remember that towers are not *forever* if you don't perform regular maintenance. If improperly installed or maintained, the tower can come down with disastrous effects.

A device called a *gin pole* is often used to place an antenna on top of a tower. If you need instructions on the use of a gin pole you should reconsider your plans. Erecting a tower and putting an antenna on its top is not a job for someone with no experience. Ron Blackburn of Tri-Ex

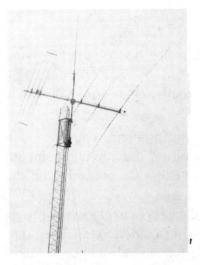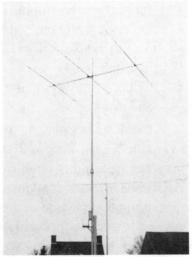

Fig 6-11—Glen Martin Engineering makes this device called a *Hazer*. Instead of climbing a tower or cranking up and down, the antenna and rotor ride up and down on the side of the tower. For maintenance, the tower stays up and the antenna comes down to meet you on the ground. *(Photo courtesy of Glen Martin Engineering)*

Fig 6-12—When not playing with his twin boys, PA3EPN can be found operating with this 40-meter Yagi on the top of an 80-foot tubular tower. The tower tilts over at the point where double section of mast ends in the photo.

Tower Corporation makes the following suggestions:

- The drawings and calculations required for local permits are usually available from the tower manufacturer.
- Compare various tower capacities both in *square feet* for wind load and in the wind speed for that loading.
- If you have questions, call the tower manufacturer's engineer. But first do your homework. This may include having a professional engineer determine the soil bearing capacity.

- Inspect tower supporting cables twice a year.
- Do not climb crank-up towers.
- Mount house brackets into the house structure—not just into the siding.
- Crank-up towers make excellent guillotines for hands and arms.

Used towers may be a major problem. They are often available for the cost of dismantling and moving them, but may be in dubious condition. Rohn Corporation and the ARRL have been cosponsoring an advertisement in *QST* that reminds everyone of the dangers of using an old tower. A used tower was probably built to older codes. Therefore it may not be used today with current building code safety requirements. Calculations and ratings may be nonexistent or incorrect due to the tower condition. Removing an old tower is a tricky process that should not be undertaken unless you have a great deal of experience.

A consultation with a local professional tower erector is very inexpensive insurance. Ask a pro before you put up or take down any tower!

Supporting Ropes and Guy Wires

Unfortunately, one of the last things most hams think of when we search out material for a new antenna are the guy wires or ropes. The choice may be made from whatever the local hardware store or discount store has in stock. Often, this is a poor choice.

Guys have two characteristics. First, they are installed under permanent tension—something is pulling on them constantly. Second, they are constantly being tortured by the weather. Sunlight, temperature extremes and salt or polluted air tend to make them lose strength as time goes on.

Many guy materials are available. They fall into two classes—conductive and nonconductive. If you are using

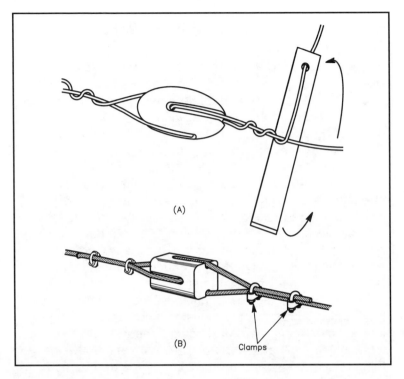

Fig 6-13—Both clamps and twisting are used for connecting guy wire. Notice the way the wires are threaded through the insulators. If the insulators should crack, the wires will remain interlocked.

guys on a large tower, local building codes and requirements will tell you what type of materials must be used. If you are looking for guy wire material for a 10-foot mast section to hold a small VHF Yagi you have a large choice of materials.

Stranded galvanized wire is readily available. Used for both small masts and as the end supports of dipoles, it is flexible and easy to use, and comes in sizes from #10 to #16. Two correct ways to fasten guy wires to an insulator are shown in Fig 6-13.

You Can Use Rope—For a While, Anyway!

Most commercially available ropes are rated in *breaking strength* and *stretch*. For antenna use, breaking strength is usually not a problem. Even the smallest readily available nylon rope, $3/16$-inch diameter, has an average breaking strength of 1200 pounds. Go up to $3/4$-inch diameter and you now can have over 16,000 pounds available to hold up that dipole.

Stretch can be a problem. Some nylon ropes will stretch almost 25% of their length when subject to a pull of half of their breaking strength. Under the same conditions, Dacron will only stretch 10%. Marine supply polypropylene stretches about the same as Dacron. Kevlar will stretch only a few per cent. Yes, this material is from the bulletproof vest family.

Kevlar is almost indestructible—except when flexed repeatedly. Under these conditions it self destructs by internal abrasion. Therefore, using it (and paying the relatively high purchase price) does not seem to be the thing to do if the Kevlar rope will go over a tree branch and constantly flex in the breeze.

Polypropylene ropes float—which does not seem very important. They also *melt* under friction—which is important. Dacron is relatively abrasion resistant, and old-fashioned braided hemp rope is very much subject to wear when abraded.

All commercial ropes are sold with a warning that they should be inspected periodically for wear. Each of them stretches, some quickly and some a little every day, until they achieve an equilibrium with the pull applied. Sunlight, temperature and chemicals in the air all take their toll. Therefore, if you use rope to hold up an antenna, plan to inspect it every few months—or just expect the rope to fail, and the antenna to fall to the ground periodically.

Various nonconductive ropes also are available. Types starting with *poly* (polyethylene, polypropylenes, polyester) all are usable, but suffer in various degrees from sunlight and chemical exposure. If you are willing and are sure you will replace these plastic ropes every few months you probably can get away with using them. The same cautions hold for nylon, manila and various cotton ropes.

A few specialized composition ropes such as one based upon *Kevlar* are advertised as not degenerating with exposure. Unfortunately, they are usually very expensive.

For these reasons, most hams opt for metal guy wires. Since they are conductive, you could ask if they will affect the antenna. Unless the guy wire is running parallel to and close to a radiating element, the answer is "usually not." Most of our antennas are so close to the ground that their patterns are distorted by the ground. If you have an 80-meter dipole 40 or 50 feet from the ground, a conductive piece of guy wire attached to the dipole end insulator will not affect the antenna pattern noticeably. In other words, for most antennas, don't worry about it!

In Your Car

Chapters 2 and 3 of this book contain a few pictures of auto mounted antennas, ranging from through-the-glass to roof- and trunk-lid-mounted units. The real challenge of these antennas is running the feed line to the rig.

Trunk-lid-mounted units allow you to route the feed line from inside the trunk, under the rear seat and beneath the bottom door trim panel to a point under the dash. Glass-mounted antennas offer fewer opportunities to hide the feed line. Usually, some part of it will be visible until you can manage to get it behind a piece of trim next to or under the window.

If you are brave or enjoy drilling a hole in a car roof—

a particularly unsettling feeling on a brand new car—a roof-mounted antenna is just the thing for you. The first step is to remove the interior dome light or overhead center console. Next rethink the entire procedure. Are you sure you really want to drill a hole in the car roof?

The roof mounts commercially available specify the hole size needed. Drill exactly that size; don't substitute the drill size you happen to have in your tool box. After installing the mount, slide the feed line under the headliner to one of the door posts. Loosening the trim screws on the door post allows the feed line to be fed down toward the floor of the car.

Plan the entire job before you drill. You may be able to install the antenna easily, but find it next to impossible to hide the feed line behind the headliner or door trim panel.

A magnetic mount is an alternative to a permanent roof mount. The feed line remains visible, both inside and outside the car. Installation takes only a few minutes, and the antenna can be quickly moved from car to car.

Be careful when you run the feed line through a window or door opening. Repeated squeezing of the feed line when the window or door is closed can damage and eventually ruin it. Try not to close the window tightly when you run the feed line though that opening.

Field Day, Camping and Hiking

The most common portable antenna consists of a dipole, a few 1-inch bolts and some light line. Use the bolts to throw a light line over a convenient tree and then hoist the ends of the dipole. All parts are lightweight and you'll have an antenna in place in only a few minutes.

Vertical antennas (for HF) are not usually used for portable operations, especially hiking and camping. Most lightweight designs, such as a $1/4$-wavelength vertical,

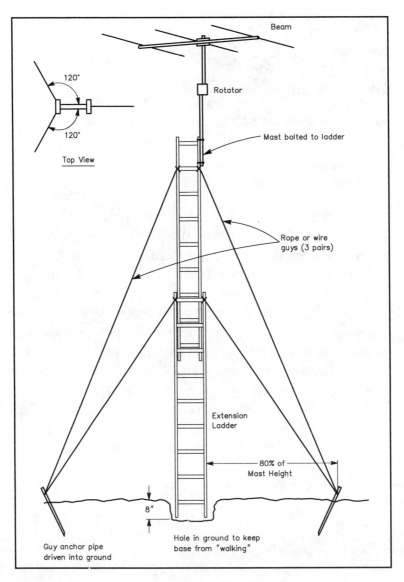

Fig 6-14—You can use an aluminum ladder for a Field Day or temporary antenna support. They are lightweight and sturdy, and can be put up with just 3 or 4 people. Fasten all guy wires to the ladder while it is still on the ground, then lever the ladder and antenna up with the ladder still in the collapsed position. Fasten the lower guys, raise the top section of the ladder, and finally fasten the top guys.

Fig 6-15—A flat plate, held down by an automobile tire, is a good temporary mast support.

require a ground system. Hikers and campers do not often want to carry ground rods and large rolls of wire for radials.

The ladder (Fig 6-14) is my favorite portable support. Many clubs use it for the annual ARRL Field Day contest. It is easily transported, since the ladder can collapse to its non-extended height. A few guy wires keep it in place, and 3 or 4 people can erect it to position a Yagi 30 or 40 feet in the air.

Another common portable support is a tower or mast section held to the ground by a piece of steel or heavy plywood. A tower section is shown in Fig 6-15, but the idea works just as well on pipe. Fasten a threaded flange to the board. Then screw a matching piece of $1\frac{1}{2}$-inch or 2-inch water pipe into the flange as the mast.

Drive your car wheel over the plate to set up a firm base wherever you are. Just don't change your mind and drive out for a sandwich during the operation!

CHAPTER 7

Stay Safe and on the Air

Emblazoned on one wall of my high school woodworking classroom in foot-high letters was a sign: **Measure Twice and Cut Once**. If I was going to apply this idea to erecting antennas, I would paraphrase it as **Plan Twice and Erect It Once!**

All hams put up antennas. The task may range from placing a magnetic mount 2-meter antenna on top of your car to erecting a 70-foot self-supporting tower with a full-size beam antenna for 30 meters. Whatever the actual task, good planning will help keep you safe.

It would not be surprising to be told that more hams were hurt in auto accidents rushing to the store before it closes than from all other antenna-related causes. Your planning should include a list of all materials you need, as well as all tools you need. Count the number of wire clamps, and have them on hand. Will two adjustable wrenches speed up the process, instead of one wrench and a pair of gas pliers? The purpose of the planning is to know what you are going to do, and what you are going to do it with.

Weather is also a problem. Although many jokes are

Table 7-1

Antenna Planning Check List
What materials are needed?
What tools are needed?
How's the weather?
Your clothing and shoes.
Safety equipment.
What do you have to do—step by step.
Are you sure you can do it, or do you need help?

made about erecting antennas in rainstorms and frigid temperatures, working on a roof or tower when they are wet is a sure recipe for disaster.

In a hurry? Don't want to take the time to put on your sneakers for the roof, or climbing boots for the tower? The minute you save now may be spent later, waiting for the response to the telephone call to 911.

Don't overreach your abilities or experience. If you need help, get a few people from the local radio club to help you. Not sure you know how to do it? Again get some help or advice. Not comfortable working at heights? Stay off the ladder, and ask a friend to do the climbing. Planning to go on an old roof? Make sure it will not collapse under you by inspecting it from beneath, in the attic.

If you need to solder outdoors use plenty of heat, and get a good connection the first time. A 25-watt iron will do for printed-circuit boards, but not for the ends of an HF dipole. Working outside with an electrical soldering iron can be a safety problem. Either use a GFI-protected outlet, or better yet buy or borrow one of the small gas-operated soldering irons now available. No extension cords, no shock hazard, and they get hot very quickly.

Table 7-1 is a checklist for antenna work. No one can

predict all the possible mistakes you can make, but if you plan the work in advance, you will be very much safer.

Towers—Go Up and Stay Safe

The previous chapter of this book, Antenna Supports, discusses safety when you put up or take down towers. In a nutshell it says if you don't have the experience, don't do it. Get qualified help. The penalty for making a mistake is very high.

Properly erected and maintained towers do a great job in placing your antennas where they should be—well clear of the ground. Therefore many hams eventually manage to put up some sort of high antenna support, and most often this is a tower. But towers also act as lightning rods for both actual lightning and neighborhood kids.

We will discuss lightning considerations in the next section. The attraction for kids is a real concern. In many areas towers and swimming pools fall into the same category, and are called *attractive nuisances*. With proper permits they are permitted on your property, but must be fenced and guarded to keep trespassers away. Many courts across the country have decided that even if you fence off your property, and place *No Trespassing* signs, you will still be partly to blame if anyone climbs the tower and is hurt.

Does that mean you should not put up a tower? No, but it does mean you should discuss it with your insurance company, and see what they say about extra coverage. Some insurance companies will be able to send you information to make your tower a little safer.

Lightning is a Problem

The lightning hazard from an antenna is often exaggerated. Ordinary amateur antennas are no more likely to

To Ground or not to Ground?

Since the early days of ham radio, antennas have been grounded to protect against the damage of a lightning strike. The idea that grounding an antenna will help prevent buildup of electrical charges is a time-honored belief, with some basis in the physics involved. According to the National Fire Protection Association, however, there is no substantial evidence to support this idea. The only sure way to be protected is to construct and ground all antennas according to the national electrical code.

Does this mean you should not ground your antennas if you don't conform with the code? Of course, connect your antennas and hardware to ground. But just remember, using a piece of #12 aluminum wire as your ground connection may not help when lightning strikes.

be hit by a direct strike than any other object of the same height in the neighborhood. Just the same, lightning does strike thousands of homes each year, so it doesn't hurt to be careful. When your station is not in use, you should ground the antenna and rotator cables, and unplug your equipment. An ungrounded antenna can pick up large electrical charges from storms in the area. These charges can damage your equipment (particularly receivers) if you don't take precautions.

Unfortunately the ground connections you make to your antenna do not conduct lightning strikes away. If your antenna is hit by lightning, most likely the antenna, feed line and nearby structures will be severely damaged. So will **you** if you insist on operating when there is a lightning storm in the area.

The ground connections help keep charges from building up on your antenna and support structures. This build-up is the usual first step of a lightning strike.

Most commercial beam and vertical antennas are grounded, for lightning protection, through the tower itself. Of course, the tower must be grounded, too. If you use a roof mount, run a heavy ground wire from the mount to a ground rod. Dipoles and end-fed wires are often not grounded. Disconnect the antenna feed line from your equipment, and use alligator-clips to connect both sides of your feed line to your station ground. It is best to ground the antenna on the outside of your home. If the energy from a lightning strike does not get into the shack, there is less danger it will flash over and destroy anything.

You can usually hear an increase in static crashes in your receiver well in advance of a thunderstorm. Be safe. When it sounds like a thunderstorm is headed your way, get off the air. If the weather forecast is for thunderstorms, don't operate! Snow and rain also generate static charges on antennas, but usually not enough to damage equipment. The best protection against lightning is to disconnect all antennas and power cords when you aren't on the air. It takes a little time to hook up everything when you want to operate again, but you will protect your station and your home if you follow this simple precaution. By the way, power companies recommend you unplug *all* electronic appliances, including TVs, VCRs and computers, when a storm threatens.

Why unplug your equipment if the antennas are disconnected? Lightning can still find its way into your equipment, through the power cord. Power lines can act as long antennas, picking up sizable charges during a storm. Simply turning off the main circuit breaker is not enough— lightning can easily jump over the circuit breaker contacts, and find its way into your equipment. The same holds true for *surge protectors*, sold as protection for home computer installations. A small jolt on the line will probably be absorbed by the surge suppresser. A full hit, if it enters your house, will not even notice the surge protector, as it vaporizes everything connected to the line or near its path.

You may decide to leave your antennas connected, and your equipment plugged in, except during peak thunderstorm months. If so, you can still protect the equipment from unexpected storms. One simple step you can take is to install a grounding switch, as shown in Fig 7-1. A small knife switch will allow you to ground your feed line, when you are not on the air. It will not disturb the normal operation of your station (with the switch open, of course!), if the lead from the feed line to the switch is no more than a couple of inches long. An alligator clip can be used instead of the switch. Whatever you use, don't forget to disconnect the ground when you transmit. This precaution is useful only on the HF bands. The switch will cause high SWR if used at VHF and UHF.

Another device that can help protect your equipment in an electrical storm is a *lightning arrestor*. It connects

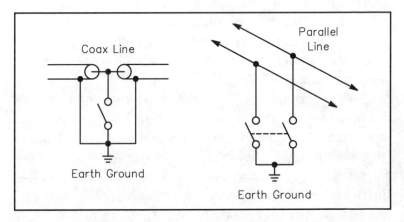

Fig 7-1—A knife switch is a very simple way to ground an antenna when it is not is use. Just be sure to remember to open up the switch before you transmit!

permanently between your feed line and the ground. When the charge on your antenna builds up to a large enough potential, the lightning arrestor will "fire." This shorts the charge to ground—not through your station. A lightning arrestor can help prevent serious damage to your equipment. Most, however, don't work fast enough to protect your station completely. Lightning arrestors are useful for commercial stations and public service (fire and police) stations, that must remain on the air regardless of the weather. **You should not rely on a lightning arrestor to protect you if you operate during a thunderstorm!**

Power Lines are Hazardous

There is one general rule when hams deal with power lines. Don't! No part of your antenna, guy wires, tower or any other piece of your installation should be able to contact a power line. This is true when you are putting your antenna up, after it is up and if it accidentally falls down. It is also true no matter how you define power lines, from the 120/240-V drop line connecting your house and the power pole in the street, to the many tens or hundreds of kilovolt transmission lines that may be in your area.

Guy wires are the easiest part of the problem. Nonconductive guy wire costs more but is fairly safe—at least during dry weather. Towers are also usually not a problem. You should locate them where they cannot hit a power line as you erect them, or (in the worst case) if they should fall in a windstorm.

HF dipoles are a real problem. In the real world, where you and I live, most HF dipoles are installed where they can fit—where there is enough room to string a piece of wire of the required length.

Here is the problem: One end of the dipole falls and comes in contact with the power line connecting the street

Fig 7-2—It may look like the result of a lightning strike, but this damage occurred when a vertical CB antenna came in contact with a nearby 34,500-V power line. Plan ahead. What would happen if your antenna came tumbling down in a storm?

power pole with your house. There now may be 120 volts or 240 volts intermittently riding on your feed line. It could be on the outside of the coax, or on the inside conductor.

Current can flow, limited only by the circuit breaker (perhaps several hundred amperes) built into the pole transformer. You don't know there is a problem. All you know is your receiver stopped working. You don't know that the power line short blew out the front end. You disconnect the coax connector and . . . *you* finish the story.

Is it worth the risk, or do you want to go back and consider some other antenna solution for your station?

There is a lot of current available when something hits the power line. Take a look at Fig 7-2. At first glance you might think the damage was done by a lighting strike. The large currents available—100 or more amperes—can do a great deal of damage. Any resulting fire can do a lot more!

RF Radiation Safety

There are many basic safety precautions to follow in

the ham shack. Being careful when working with high voltage, sharp tools and hot soldering irons is one obvious example. Another important concern, one often overlooked, is RF safety. This involves minimizing human exposure to strong radio-frequency fields. These potentially dangerous fields occur near or around antennas.

Biological effects of RF exposure have been studied for several decades. We know body tissues, subjected to large amounts of RF energy, may suffer damage. It is possible to receive an RF burn from touching an antenna used for transmitting. You don't have to come into direct contact with an antenna to damage body tissues, however. Just being present in a strong RF field can cause problems.

Taken to extremes, we could compare the effects of RF exposure to the way a microwave oven cooks food. A typical microwave oven uses a 500-watt RF source operating at 2450 MHz. The Technician/Novice 1270-MHz band is about half this frequency, and so can have similar effects. Of course, the microwave oven is designed to concentrate its RF power for heating food, and is not directly comparable to Amateur Radio operations. Some studies have shown that persons who are exposed to strong RF fields, over a period of time, may be at increased risk to develop certain kinds of cancer.

There is no cause for alarm in most amateur installations. But be aware that exposure to strong RF fields—which we cannot see, smell, hear or touch—can cause health risks.

The amount of RF energy that the body absorbs depends on the radio frequency. The body absorbs RF energy most efficiently in the VHF range (30 to 300 MHz). Absorption is greatest if the antenna orientation is parallel to the body (vertically polarized). Sensitive parts of the body, such as the eyes, are particularly prone to damage from RF energy.

Most amateur operation is with relatively low RF power, and is intermittent—the transmitter is not operating continuously. Hams spend more time listening than transmitting. If you use modes such as RTTY and FM, where the RF carrier is present continuously at full power, you'll need to pay more attention to RF safety.

RF Safety Guidelines

Take the time to study and follow these general guidelines to minimize your exposure to RF fields. Most of these guidelines are just common sense, and good amateur practice.

Confine RF radiation to the antenna, where it belongs. Provide a good earth ground for your equipment. Particularly at VHF and UHF, poor-quality feed line and improperly installed connectors can be a source of unwanted RF radiation. Use only good-quality coaxial cable. Be sure the connectors are of good quality, and are properly installed. Good-quality coaxial cable and connectors will also help reduce RF loses in your system.

Don't operate RF power amplifiers or transmitters with the covers or shielding removed. This practice helps you avoid both electric shock hazards and RF safety hazards. A safety interlock prevents the gear from being turned on accidentally, while the shielding is off. This is especially important for VHF and UHF equipment. When reassembling transmitting equipment, replace all the screws that hold the RF compartment shielding in place. Tighten all the screws securely before applying power to the equipment.

In high-power operation in the HF and VHF region, keep the antenna away from people. Humans should not be allowed within 10 to 15 feet of vertical antennas. This is especially important with higher power, high-duty-cycle operation (such as FM or RTTY). Amateur antennas that are mounted on towers and masts, away from people, pose no exposure problem. Always install your antennas where people and animals cannot touch them.

When using mobile equipment with 10 watts of RF power output or more, do not transmit if anyone is standing within 2 feet of the antenna. The best location for a VHF/UHF mobile antenna—from an RF safety standpoint and for the best radiated-signal pattern—is in the middle of the automobile roof. This position also protects the car's occupants.

When using a hand-held transceiver, with RF power output of several watts or more, maintain at least 1 to 2 inches separation between the antenna and your forehead, to protect your eyes. It is recommended that hand-held radios have a power of no more than 7 watts. *This does not mean it is safe to use a 7-watt hand-held transceiver at all times and under all conditions.* If 1 watt or ¹/₂-watt will do, why take any extra risk? Use the lowest possible power, and the greatest possible separation of the antenna from your body.

Never touch an antenna that has RF power applied. Be sure RF power is

Fig 7-3—This parabolic antenna looks harmless, but you can get hurt if you stand in the path of the transmitted power. David Hallidy, KD5RO, built this unit for use on 1296 MHz. Notice it is pointed up and away from any people! *(Photo courtesy of David Hallidy)*

Table 7-2

RF Awareness Guidelines

Although antennas on towers (well away from people) pose no exposure problem, make certain that the RF radiation is confined to the antenna radiating elements themselves. Provide a single good station ground, and eliminate radiation from transmission lines. Use good quality coax cable, not open-wire transmission lines or end-fed antennas that come directly into the shack.

No person should ever be near any transmitting antenna when it is in use. This is especially true from mobile and ground-mounted vertical antennas. Avoid transmitting with more than 25 watts in a VHF mobile installation, unless it is possible to first measure the field inside the vehicle. At the 1-kilowatt level both HF and VHF directional antennas should be at least 35 feet above inhabited areas. Avoid using indoor and attic mounted antennas, if at all possible.

Don't operate RF power amplifiers with the covers removed, especially at VHF/UHF.

In the UHF/SHF region, never look into the open end of an activated length of waveguide, or point it toward anyone. Never point a high-gain narrow-beamwidth antenna (a parabolic dish, for instance) toward people. Make sure the correct waveguide flanges are used, and they are properly mated to prevent leakage at the joints.

With hand-held transceivers, keep the antenna away from your head, and use the lowest possible power to maintain communications. Use a separate microphone, and hold the rig as far away from you as possible.

Don't work on antennas that have RF power applied.

Don't stand or sit close to a linear amplifier power supply when the power is turned on. Stay at least 24 inches away from power transformers, electrical fans and other sources of high-level 60-Hz magnetic fields.

off, and stays off, before working on or adjusting an antenna. Also, make sure any nearby antennas are deactivated. Never have someone else transmit into the antenna and monitor the SWR, while you are making adjustments. When matching an antenna, you should turn the transmitter off, and then make the adjustment. Now back away to a safe distance, before turning the transmitter on again, to check your work.

During transmissions, never point a high-gain UHF or microwave antenna (such as a parabolic dish) toward people or animals (Fig 7-3). Never look into the open end of a UHF or microwave waveguide feed line that is carrying RF power. Never point the open end of a UHF waveguide that is carrying RF power toward people or animals. Make sure all waveguide connections are tightly secured.

What Does the ARRL Do?

For many years volunteer members or the ARRL have provided their professional expertise and guidance in the area of health and RF radiation. Table 7-2 was developed by one group to provide guidance. It is based on measurements made by the FCC and the Environmental Protection Agency (EPA) in 1990. The Resources Guide at the end of this book lists sources of additional information. You can also contact the ARRL Technical Information Service (TIS) for more information. The ARRL TIS is described in the Resources Guide.

Remember: The FCC, the EPA and ARRL volunteers can only give you guidance. They serve to put up road warning signs. Just as it is up to you to drive safely, it is also up to you to use transmitters safely.

Other Problems in Our Electronic World

We live in a very complicated electronic world. A few years ago houses had doorbells—now many have electronic touch plates, intruder alarms and microprocessor-controlled locks. As a result, there are a few other safety-related issues you should know about.

Vehicles and their Microprocessors

Today's vehicles have a large amount of electronics. Although they are supposedly well tested, the manufacturers do make mistakes. After all, how often did you have to take your last new car back to the dealer to fix "one or two little things." Occasionally a car will come along that is sensitive to RF energy. It's best to find this problem *before* you are driving down the turnpike or freeway at 65 MPH. Pressing the push-to-talk button has been known to make a car stall or misfire, as the RF interferes with the microprocessor-controlled ignition system.

Before you install a new mobile rig, connect the antenna and rig temporarily to see if there is any effect. Remember some automotive transmissions are also electronically (actually software) controlled. Although the probability of interference with these computer-controlled units is small, it can happen. Therefore, first test your new installation at home, and then on a quiet back road.

Hospitals are Full of Electronics

There is probably no place with more exotic electronics than today's hospitals. Automatic body pumps, heart monitors and many other devices are spread from one end of the floor to the other. Until recently, cellular telephones, paging devices and hand-held radios (belonging to nurses and security staff members) transmitted freely around the building. So did hams who were either visiting fellow hams, in waiting rooms or unfortunately resident as patients.

It is obviously not a good idea to allow all this radiation near sensitive equipment. The equipment may give incorrect readings or malfunction completely. Recently, many hospitals have been restricting the use of these small transmitters. At the same time, more and more electronic medical devices are being used at home for long-term treatment of patients. If anyone in your home is using an electronically controlled or powered device, such as a pacemaker, make sure it is not affected by your transmitter before you inadvertently interfere with someone's health. Talk to the doctor and the manufacturer of the device. Play it safe! The DX will wait until the patient recovers a bit, and there is always your club station or a friend's house.

Airline Restrictions

It sounds like a good idea at first. There you sit, in a window seat, cruising along at 25,000 feet. Just press to talk, and every ham monitoring 146.52 in 15 states will respond.

You may *think* it is a good idea, but the airlines definitely don't agree. All airlines ban the use of transmitters and receivers without specific permission of the pilot (and often the airline). They are concerned that your transmitter, and even the oscillator in your receiver, will radiate sufficiently to affect the aircraft's communications and navigation systems.

The rules are even changing on laptop computers and video games. Several airlines now ban their use during take-off and landing. Everyone would rather get from New York to Chicago safely. So forget your hand-held rig for a few hours; that contact will wait!

Resources Guide

I n this section you will find references to other useful books and materials on the always fascinating subject of ham antennas (and related areas). There is also additional information on some of the topics covered in this book, listed by chapter. A description of all the antenna-related books and software sold by the ARRL appears at the end of the Resources Guide.

A Few Basic Resources

The **American Radio Relay League (ARRL)**, publisher of this book (and many others on all aspects of Amateur Radio) has been serving ham radio operators and others since 1914. ARRL represents the interests of Amateur Radio in Washington, DC, and around the world, it publishes the most widely respected ham magazine, *QST*, transmits code practice and bulletins over W1AW and sponsors a number of operating events.

ARRL
225 Main St
Newington, CT 06111-1494 USA
Voice: 860-594-0200
Fax: 860-594-0259
E-mail: tis@arrl.org
Automated Information Server: info@arrl.org

The most popular and reliable source of all things amateur is *The ARRL Handbook for Radio Amateurs.* Updated every year, it can be found in the ham shacks of virtually all active hams, as well as in many libraries, engineering companies and technical schools. If you are just getting interested in Amateur Radio, or want to find more information on antennas, this book has it all. You will find chapters on antenna theory, design and construction, radio-wave propagation and transmission lines.

As it's been since the 1930s, *The ARRL Antenna Book* is the premier book on antennas. The current edition has over 700 pages packed with antenna theory and practical information, plus a computer disk. If you have a problem or question about antennas, feed lines or propagation, you'll find the answer here.

The ARRL's *Now You're Talking!* is a complete study guide for those preparing for their first license. It contains practical antenna information as well as construction projects, all aimed at newcomers.

Although its emphasis is on operating, *The ARRL Operating Manual* is ideal for those setting up their first station. It also has detailed information on using antennas and equipment on all amateur modes and popular activities.

If you are thinking about buying a commercial antenna or a used antenna accessory such as a tuner or rotator (or for that matter any other piece of gear), check out the two volumes of *The ARRL Radio Buyer's Sourcebook*. They contain the Product Reviews published in *QST*, and can give you the valuable insight and guidance you will need before you head for the flea market or radio store.

QST, the official journal of the American Radio Relay League, is sent monthly to members. This is where you will find new and exciting ideas on antennas and every other topic of interest to hams. For membership information, contact the League at the address or telephone number above. The ads in *QST* are another good source of information. If you want to know what is available and where to get it, just spend a few minutes thumbing through the ads.

Another valuable source of antenna designs is *The ARRL Antenna Compendium* series. There are currently four volumes available, with more to come. They contain previously unpublished articles on new antenna projects as well as transmission lines and propagation. Hams who think they have a unique antenna-related problem often find the answer in these books.

Following this section is a list of ARRL antenna publications. For the latest publications catalog, contact the ARRL, or look in the back of the latest issue of *QST*.

Sources of Parts and Equipment

The References chapter of *The ARRL Handbook* contains a comprehensive list of antenna and other equipment suppliers, including addresses and other contact information. This list is updated annually. Each of the manufacturers whose products are shown in this book are listed in *The Handbook*.

If you use e-mail, you can get helpful information from the ARRL Automated Mail Server. Address a message to info@arrl.org. The text of your message should contain a single word HELP (use just the four letters, without punctuation or anything else). You will receive, by e-mail, instructions on how to use the Automated Information Server, along with an abbreviated list of available files. If you send a message consisting only of the word INDEX, you'll receive a file listing all currently available files.

More Info from the ARRL

Although the ARRL Technical Information Service is designed primarily for members, all radio amateurs can contact the ARRL for information. In addition to the mail, telephone and fax numbers listed earlier in this Resources Guide, the ARRL has a computer bulletin board and several FTP sites.

To use the telephone BBS, set your computer modem to the standard 8-n-1 parameters and call 860-594-0306. Follow the on-screen directions, and you will be logged onto HIRAM, the computer bulletin board. Up-to-date addresses, information files and software are available. The system will tell you how to download files or other information. If you have FTP capability though the internet, FTP to mgate.arrl.org and retrieve the file helpinfo.txt in the /pub directory.

Chapter 1

The **propagation charts** published in *QST* are part of the monthly feature *How's DX?* The usual page contains 30 charts, and covers most areas of the world. The bottom of each chart is the time in UTC. To use a chart, you must convert your local time to UTC. The sidebar describes this process.

The charts are constructed using a sophisticated program called IONCAP. Fortunately, we do not have to understand this program to use the charts, but a little knowledge would not hurt. The propagation chapter of *The*

Handbook is a good place to start. It includes a band-by-band summary of the typical propagation characteristics you will find on each of the amateur bands. *The ARRL Operating Manual*, in the chapter on basic operating, contains a good summary of how to pick a band when you want to operate.

Chapter 2

If you are interested in **working VHF or UHF stations** *direct*—without a repeater—and want more information on high-gain antennas, *The ARRL Antenna Book* is the place to start. It has a chapter on VHF/UHF antennas that includes Yagis (beams), quads, corner reflectors, stacked arrays, parabolic dishes and just about every other high-performance antenna. It also includes practical building instructions, to allow you to duplicate the antennas described in the text.

For those whose needs are more modest, and who want to talk to the local group on FM with or without a repeater, the **J-pole** described in Chapter 2 is a good bet. The balun discussed in the chapter uses the Amidon 2X-43-251 split core cylindrical ferrite bead, made of #43 material. Mount the bead about 19 inches from the feedpoint, around the coax feed line.

As discussed in the chapter, if a large hill or building is in the way, even a very high performance antenna may not help very much. To predict this problem in advance, you can use US government maps to plot the **line of sight**. The repeater chapter of *The Handbook* contains directions for finding the line of sight.

Chapter 3

Discussions about **connecting coax cable** to a dipole, without a coax connector, are found in several places in this

UTC Explained

Ever hear of Greenwich Mean Time? How about Coordinated Universal Time? Do you know if it is light or dark at 0400 hours? If you answered no to any of these questions, read on!

Keeping track of time can be pretty confusing when you are talking to other hams around the world. Europe, for example, is anywhere from 4 to 11 hours ahead of us here in North America. Over the years, the time at Greenwich, England, has been universally recognized as the standard time in all international affairs, including ham radio. (We measure longitude on the surface of the Earth in degrees east or west of the Prime Meridian, which runs through Greenwich, and which is halfway around the world from the International Date Line.) This means that wherever you are, you and the station you contact will be able to reference a common date and time easily. Mass confusion would occur if everyone used their own local time.

Coordinated Universal Time (abbreviated UTC) is the name for what used to be called Greenwich Mean Time.

book. The dipole described in Chapter 3 uses this type of connection.

Fig 5-15 contains the instructions for stripping the end of the coax and preparing it to be connected. *Take your time.* Use a very sharp knife, gently. You don't want to cut through any of the braid. If you do cut a few strands, don't panic, but if you cut more than a few, consider starting over. As Chapter 3 discusses in detail, when soldering, go in, solder quickly and remove the soldering iron! Again, the faster

UTC	EDT/AST	CDT/EST	MDT/CST	PDT/MST	PST
0000*	2000	1900	1800	1700	1600
0100	2100	2000	1900	1800	1700
0200	2200	2100	2000	1900	1800
0300	2300	2200	2100	2000	1900
0400	0000*	2300	2200	2100	2000
0500	0100	0000*	2300	2200	2100
0600	0200	0100	0000*	2300	2200
0700	0300	0200	0100	0000*	2300
0800	0400	0300	0200	0100	0000*
0900	0500	0400	0300	0200	0100
1000	0600	0500	0400	0300	0200
1100	0700	0600	0500	0400	0300
1200	0800	0700	0600	0500	0400
1300	0900	0800	0700	0600	0500
1400	1000	0900	0800	0700	0600
1500	1100	1000	0900	0800	0700
1600	1200	1100	1000	0900	0800
1700	1300	1200	1100	1000	0900
1800	1400	1300	1200	1100	1000
1900	1500	1400	1300	1200	1100
2000	1600	1500	1400	1300	1200
2100	1700	1600	1500	1400	1300
2200	1800	1700	1600	1500	1400
2300	1900	1800	1700	1600	1500
2400	2000	1900	1800	1700	1600

*0000 and 2400 are interchangeable. 2400 is associated with the date of the day ending, 0000 with the day just starting.

you solder the connections, the less likely you will melt some of the coax insulation. That is why you should use a 100-watt or larger iron. Don't try for perfection. The various plastics used in coax usually melt easily, so try to hold everything straight and still until the soldered joint cools. Gas-operated soldering irons have several advantages: no extension cord, and no worries about where to put a hot electrical iron in your backyard, as you wait until it cools after use.

I have twice had **problems with water** going down the *inside* of a coax feed line. No, I really didn't believe it would happen, until I found a puddle on my operating desk. There were no kids at home to blame, and my clue was the water that spilled out of the rig when I tried to move it out of the puddle.

The combination of 3M *Super 33+ Vinyl Tape* followed by 3M *Scotchkote* is a good one. Many hams feel it is the best way to keep water out for a long time. The easy way, using one of the putty compounds sold to seal outdoor connectors, may work, but the reports are mixed. Some hams have had great success, while others have had great problems.

This chapter urges you to look at the **requirements for amateur antennas** in *The National Electrical Code*, published by The National Fire Protection Association. Many, if not most, states require builders and electricians to comply with this code, to ensure the safety of their structures. The Safety chapter in *The ARRL Handbook* has more information.

For more information on **HF Yagis, quads and V-beams**, see *The ARRL Antenna Book*. It has full chapters on multielement antennas (Yagis), quads, and other high performance antennas. If you are interested in constructing an **inductively loaded dipole**, The *Antenna Book* has information and instructions.

The topic of **short-wave listening**—SWLing—was touched upon briefly. This is a hobby within a hobby. Many hams participate in the search for unusual and often distant stations. This is even more true when propagation conditions are poor, such as at the low part of the sunspot cycle. *The ARRL Operating Manual* has a chapter on SWLing, including suggested bands and frequencies. You can search out both broadcast stations, such as those for various overseas countries, and action stations, such as those transmitting from Coast Guard ships, the presidential aircraft fleet and anti-drug forces.

Chapter 4

The References chapter in *The Handbook* contains the **current addresses** of MFJ and all other ham equipment and parts suppliers. This list is updated annually. A second good source is *QST*. Each month, on one of the last pages, is an Index of Advertisers. Find the company you are interested in contacting, turn to the page listed for the company's ad, and you will find the most current address and telephone numbers.

A full description of the **flagpole antenna** is in *The ARRL Antenna Book*, 17th edition, on page 6-19. It is a good choice for a hidden antenna. Few people will complain about an attractive flagpole in your yard.

The **Shorty Forty** antenna uses Miniductor #3029. If you would like, you can "roll your own." The coil consists of #12 wire wound at 6 turns per inch. A 30-turn coil, as needed for the Shorty Forty, would be 30 ÷ 6 or 5 inches long. Wind it on any plastic form or section of pipe with an outside diameter of $2^1/2$ inches. Since the antenna will be mounted in an attic, weatherproofing is not necessary.

Chapter 5

You will find more information on **lightning protection** in the first chapter of *The ARRL Antenna Book*, 17th edition. This chapter can save you considerable grief (and money). Another source of protection information is *The National Electrical Code,* discussed earlier. The material is not always the easiest to understand, but it is the industrial "bible" for construction practices.

Installing coax connectors on a length of coax is not difficult, if you follow the manufacturer's instructions. Solder-on

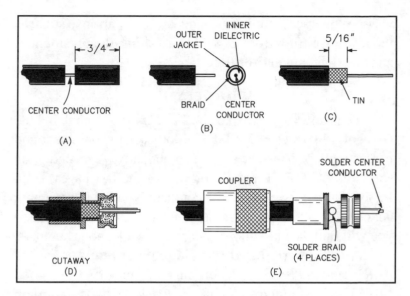

Fig RG-1—Follow these steps to put a PL-259 connector on the end of a piece of coax. This figure shows the process for RG-8 and similar sized coax.

1) Cut ³/₄ of an inch of the outer cover, shield and inner insulator (A). Make your cut deep enough to remove all this material down to the center conductor. You now should just have ³/₄ inch of center conductor showing (B). Be careful when you cut not to nick the center conductor.

2) Cut and remove an additional ⁵/₁₆ inch of the outer cover. Your cable end should now look like (C). Tin the exposed braid quickly, being careful not to melt the inner insulating material.

3) Slide the outer coupler ring over the coax. Position it so the knurled end is toward the cable end (E). If you forget this one, you will have to cut off the connector and start over.

4) Screw the connector body onto the cable (E). If you cut everything correctly, the center conductor will just protrude from the center barrel of the connector.

5) With a large soldering iron apply heat to the center of the connector, and flow solder into each of the four solder holes. Don't be afraid to apply a large amount of heat—just don't bend the coax, so if it does start to melt it will resolidify in a straight line.

6) Allow the connector to cool well, and then solder the center pin. Solder will flow up the pin. After this connection cools, cut (if necessary) and file the end tip smooth.

7) Screw the coupler (outer knurled sleeve) down over the connector.

connectors are fine for amateur work. Do not use consumer pushon types. They can lead to poor connections and, after a while, may generate television and other interference due to corrosion in the joints. Fig RG-1 includes instructions for **attaching a standard PL-259 to RG-8** (approximately ¹/₂-inch diameter) coax. Fig RG-2 covers the use of **adapters** with the smaller (RG-58 or -59) coax sizes.

Fig RG-2—If you want to use RG-58, RG-59 or other small coax, you must use a matched adapter to connect it to a PL-259 connector.

83-1SP (PL-259) PLUG WITH ADAPTERS (UG-176/U OR UG-175/U)

COUPLING RING   ADAPTER

1) Cut end of cable even. Remove vinyl jacket 3/4" — don't nick braid. Slide coupling ring and adapter on cable.

2) Fan braid slightly and fold back over cable.

3) Position adapter to dimension shown. Press braid down over body of adapter and trim to 3/8". Bare 5/8" of conductor. Tin exposed center conductor.

PLUG ASSEMBLY   SOLDER HOLE

4) Screw the plug assembly on adapter. Solder braid to shell through solder holes. Solder conductor to contact sleeve.

5) Screw coupling ring on plug assembly.

Ferrite beads are available from several suppliers (see the notes on suppliers, above). Most companies who sell antennas and antenna parts, wire and coax stock these beads.

Chapter 6

The ARRL has a **Technical Information Service**, or TIS, for the use of members and other hams. The contact addresses in the first part of this chapter tell you how to get this information. The best way is electronic, through the internet or the **ARRL telephone BBS**. Once you find the information file of interest, you can immediately download it. *The Handbook* contains a list of text files available from TIS on a wide variety of problems and topics.

If you are thinking about **erecting a tower**, and need information on **PRB-1**, the FCC ruling that gives hams a valuable tool in fighting restrictive local antenna ordinances, contact the ARRL Regulatory Information Branch. Information about PRB-1 also appears in the ARRL publication *The FCC Rule Book.*

Chapter 7

The ARRL Technical Information Service (TIS), discussed earlier in this Resources Guide, has a number of information files on **RF safety**. Both *The Handbook* and *The ARRL Antenna Book* also have extensive safety coverage.

ARRL Antenna Books, Other Publications and Software

Contact the American Radio Relay League, 225 Main St, Newington, CT 06111-1494 for the latest prices and ordering information. The telephone number is 860-594-0200.

The ARRL Antenna Book is the definitive source for

information on state-of-the-art antenna and transmission line theory and construction. It presents the best and most highly regarded coverage of antenna fundamentals, propagation, transmission lines, Yagis and quads, as well as all popular wire antenna designs. The chapter on HF Yagi Arrays is based on the latest computer modeling software. The Radio Wave Propagation chapter contains comprehensive statistical data on the range of elevation angles needed for communication from all areas of the US to important DX locations. Included is a 1.44 MB 3.5-inch diskette for the IBM PC/XT/AT and compatible computers with software by K6STI, W1FM and N6BV for Yagi analysis, propagation prediction, transmission-line evaluation, and more.

©1994, 736 pages, #4734 $30

Four volumes are available in *The ARRL Antenna Compendium* series, and each is packed with previously unpublished articles on all the popular types of HF/VHF/UHF antennas and some you've never heard of! In Volume 1 you'll find articles on a multiband portable, quads and loops, baluns and the Smith Chart. Volume 2 features several verticals, an attic tribander, antenna modeling and propagation. Among the 40 articles in Volume 3, you'll discover a 12-meter quad, a discone, modeling with MININEC and VHF/UHF ray tracing. Volume 4 includes articles on 80 and 160 meters, mobile work, portable or temporary antennas and modeling. Bundled in Volume 4 is an IBM-format, 3.5-inch, 720-kB disk with source data used in modeling and executable programs relating to some of the antennas described in the book (modeling software not included). All four volumes are a feast for the antenna enthusiast! Companion software is available separately for Volumes 2 and 3.

Volume 1, ©1985, 176 pages, #0194 $10

Volume 2, ©1989, 216 pages, #2545 $14
  Companion software (5.25-inch) #2626 $10
Volume 3, ©1992, 240 pages, #4017 $14
  Companion software (5.25-inch) #4033 $10
  Companion software (3.5-inch) #4041 $10
Volume 4, ©1995, 224 pages plus software #4912 $20

Antennas and Techniques for Low Band DXing, by noted DXer John Devoldere, ON4UN, is an in-depth treatment of the antennas and operating strategies you'll need to span the continents on 40, 80 and 160 meters. You'll find operating tips, antenna designs and optional software culled both from the author's years of experience and those of other active DXers, contesters and antenna experimenters.
  Revised and expanded 2nd Ed., ©1994, 400 pages, #4661 $20

Low-Profile Amateur Radio is for the ham who lives where antennas are frowned upon. You'll see that you don't need a house with acreage to enjoy your favorite hobby. One practical solution: hide your antennas. Another: operate with low power. This book tells you how to get on the air using these techniques and others without calling attention to yourself.
  Softcover, 1st Ed., ©1993, 128 pages, #4114 $8

ARRL MicroSmith V2.00, by Wes Hayward, W7ZOI. *ARRL MicroSmith* is a Smith Chart simulation program for the IBM PC and compatibles. You don't need detailed knowledge of the Smith Chart. Use *MicroSmith* to design matching networks with fixed or variable L-C components, stub-matching sections with transmission lines, and more. It's all done graphically on your computer screen. It's also useful for a variety of network analysis problems. Includes a 48-page user's guide with numerous illustrations.
  3.5-inch diskette #4084 $39

Practical Wire Antennas, by John D. Heys, G3BDQ, is an RSGB book that delves into the practical aspects of HF wire antennas: how the various types work, and how to buy or build one that's right for you. Marconis, Windoms, loops, dipoles and even underground antennas—they're all covered! The final chapter covers matching systems.

©1989, 100 pages, #R878 $14

HF Antennas for All Locations, written by L. A. Moxon, G6XN, for the RSGB, details the design and construction of hundreds of amateur antennas, including some unusual designs. Don't let a lack of real estate keep you off the air. Whether you're in a downtown apartment or on top of a mountain, you'll find at least one antenna that'll work for you!

2nd Ed., ©1993, 322 pages, #4300 $35

HF Antenna Collection contains outstanding articles from RSGB's *RadCom*. It covers single- and multielement horizontal and vertical antennas, very small transmitting and receiving antennas, feeders, tuners and more.

©1991, 240 pages, #3770 $18

The ARRL UHF/Microwave Experimenter's Manual is written for the growing number of radio amateurs who are discovering that there is life on our frequencies above 420 MHz. Technicians and engineers will find this book particularly useful. You'll find information on design and fabrication techniques, propagation, antennas and feed lines, transmission media and much more. Companion software is available for IBM PCs and compatibles.

Book, 1st Ed., ©1990, 448 pages, #3126 $20
Software (3.5-inch) #4726 $10

The ARRL UHF/Microwave Projects Manual contains dozens of construction articles for transverters, preamplifiers, power amplifiers, antennas, and test and measurement equipment. Some articles are previously unpublished; others are reprinted from conference proceedings, *QST* and *QEX*. If your interest lies in the bands above 432 MHz, you'll find this book to be invaluable.
Book, 1st Ed., ©1994, 352 pages, #4491 $20

Beyond Line of Sight: A History of VHF Propagation from the Pages of QST explores the ways hams helped discover and exploit the propagation modes that allow VHF signals to travel hundreds and even thousands of miles. It's a subject all hams will find fascinating.
Book, 1st Ed., ©1992, 234 pages, #4025 $12

Radio Auroras by Charlie Newton, G2FKZ, from the RSGB, details the interesting and unpredictable world of Amateur Radio communications via auroral propagation. Presented with a European twist is information on what causes auroras, how they are forecast and how to best use them to work DX. You'll find an abundance of tables and charts.
Book, ©1991, 96 pages, #3568 $18

Microwave Handbook, Volume 1, from RSGB, covers operating techniques, system analysis and propagation, microwave antennas, transmission line and components, microwave semiconductors and tubes.
Book, ©1989, 200 pages, #2901 $35

Microwave Handbook, Volume 2, from RSGB, continues where Volume 1 leaves off with construction techniques, common equipment, microwave beacons and repeaters, test equipment, safety, filters and additional circuit data.
Book, ©1991, 244 pages, #3606 $35

Microwave Handbook, Volume 3, from RSGB, contains a review of microwave theory and practice, reference information, practical designs, hints and tips. Covers 1.3-24 GHz.

Book, ©1992, 284 pages, #3975 $35

Antenna and Transmission Line Design Aids
Standard Smith Charts (package of 5 sheets) ......#1340 $2
Expanded Smith Charts (package of 5 sheets) .....#1350 $2
Smith Charts—50-ohm center, (package of 5
    sheets) ....#1341 $2
Antenna Pattern Worksheets, 100 8.5" × 11"
    sheets ....#1360 $3

Other ARRL Publications and Services

QST—ARRL'S Monthly Membership Journal

Simply put, *QST* is the best source of news and practical information from the world of Amateur Radio. Hams and others interested in Amateur Radio from North America and around the world find it indispensable. *QST* comes with your ARRL membership. Here's some of what you'll find in each issue:

The New Ham Companion section features articles on all aspects of ham radio, from the viewpoint of the less-experienced ham.

Technical Articles provide fascinating theory and practical designs that will expand your Amateur Radio horizons.

Product Reviews present comprehensive yet readable reports on the latest transceivers and accessories; only *QST* product reviews are based on careful and comprehensive testing done in the ARRL Lab and painstaking field testing.

Hints & Kinks are clever and useful tips sent in by *QST* readers who have found a better way to accomplish a task or solve a problem. You never know what you'll find each month, but you can be sure you'll find something practical and imaginative.

DXing/Contesting, two of the most popular on-the-air activities, are covered in detail in each issue. The How's DX? column provides profiles of well-known DXers and hints on getting more out of your station. ARRL-sponsored contests are fun ways of seeing how your station stacks up against others.

Feature articles cover all the fascinating aspects of ham radio, from a colorful DXpedition on a rare atoll, to a personal story of how a ham introduced her family to the wonders of her favorite hobby.

Ham Ads and display ads are the best way to find a piece of Amateur Radio gear, new or used, top shelf or barebones. Whether it's a new 20-meter beam or a computer program that teaches the Morse code, you'll find it advertised in *QST*.

Useful and timely news, from the FCC or the international scene, is included in articles and columns like League Lines and Happenings. If it's happening, you'll learn about it by reading *QST*.

Single issue price is $5. Contact the ARRL for complete membership information.

Handy References

The ARRL Handbook for Radio Amateurs will place you on the cutting edge of Amateur Radio technology. An indispensable reference, the *Handbook* has been the "ham's bible" since 1926. It contains a wealth of information on subjects ranging from analog electronic theory to transceivers, repeaters to DSP, circuit construction to interference, transmission lines to antennas and propagation. The *Handbook* is many things:

- a ham radio reference guide that includes tables and charts hams need and use most often
- a guide to radio theory every ham should know, including the latest digital modes and hundreds of explanatory and practical circuits
- a goldmine of construction projects that will allow all hams—beginners, old-timers and everyone in between—to build useful amateur gear for their stations

In the Modes chapter, you'll find an overview of the many ways hams communicate, from the on/off keying of Morse code to the complex but powerful digital techniques that will define Amateur Radio communication into the next century. Whether you're an experienced builder or a neophyte, you'll find the Circuit Construction chapter useful as it takes you from schematic to finished project.

The AC/RF Sources chapter explains, clearly and concisely, modern oscillator and synthesizer design. Mathematics for Amateur Radio provides a refresher course in the math concepts that form the basis of ham radio and electronics.

The Station Setup and Accessories chapter shows how to set up or enhance your station for top performance; among other projects, includes a boom/headset mike and three computer interfaces. In the Transceivers chapter, you'll learn about the systems and design that go into modern radio equipment. Projects include a beginner's shortwave receiver, QRP transceivers and a 50-W solid-state linear amplifier.

If it's ham radio, it's in the ARRL *Handbook*. With over 1200 pages and over 1000 charts and illustrations, it's an exceptional value.

Softcover. Annual........#1735 $38 including software.

The ARRL Radio Buyer's Sourcebooks are for anyone who buys, sells or owns Amateur Radio equipment. Two volumes are available: The ARRL *Radio Buyer's Sourcebook* covers selected *QST* Product Reviews from 1981 through 1991 and a few golden oldies. The ARRL *Radio Buyer's Sourcebook Volume 2* contains all *QST* Product Reviews published in 1991 and 1992.

Both books explain what radios do, how well they do it, where to get them serviced and where to find articles about modifications. Handy comparative feature and performance charts cover equipment reviewed in the books. Each contains a history of Amateur Radio technology and a glossary of radio features and terms. Heading for a hamfest or ham dealer? Don't leave home without both *Radio Buyer's Sourcebooks*.

The ARRL Radio Buyer's Sourcebook, ©1991, 384 pages, #3452 $15

The ARRL Radio Buyer's Sourcebook Volume 2, ©1993, 240 pages, #4211 $15

Antenna-Speak Glossary

Antenna—A device that picks up or sends out radio signals. A full *antenna system* includes towers, supports, mounts, feed lines and everything needed to keep the antenna in the air and connected to your rig.

Antenna analyzer—A test instrument used to make SWR and other measurements of an antenna (and feed line).

Antenna tuners—Some books call them antenna matching units, tuners, match boxes or Transmatches—are units designed to connect a feed line to a rig, or a feed line to an antenna, with minimum loss in the entire system. These matching networks usually consist of 2 or 3 variable inductors and capacitors.

Azimuth angle—Just as in navigation of a ship, this is the angle to the place you (or your signal) want to go. True north is usually the reference (0°), east is 90° and so on.

Balun—Contraction for balanced to unbalanced. A device to couple a balanced load to an unbalanced source, or vice versa. They are used both as a matching device and to control the flow of current in transmission lines. Common types are current choke baluns, voltage baluns and bead baluns.

Base station antenna—Term taken from some commercial radio services and CB radio. Most hams would refer to their antenna as being at their *home QTH* or at a *fixed location*.

Beam antenna—See **Yagi**.

Boom—The center support of a Yagi or quad. The elements mount on the boom, and the boom is connected to the rotating vertical shaft or mast.

Characteristic impedance—A number that describes the electrical properties of an antenna feed line. It is a result of the resistance, inductance and capacitance of the conductors used and their physical arrangement. Common values are 50 and 72 ohms for coax, 300 ohms for TV-type line and 450 ohms for open wire line and ladder line.

Coaxial cable—Coax (pronounced kó-aks). A type of feed line with one conductor inside the other. The center axis of both conductors is the same, thus the name *coaxial*, shortened to coax.

Counterpoise—A partly obsolete term that describes the use of one or more wires run under an antenna in place of a ground system.

dB or decibels—The units used to describe the relative strength of signals.

Dipole antenna—See **Half-wave dipole**. A dipole need not be $^1/_2$ wavelength long.

Direct—See **Repeater**

Directivity—The ability of an antenna to focus transmitter power into certain directions. Also its ability to enhance received signals from specific directions.

Director—An element in front of the driven element in a Yagi and some other types of directional antennas.

Driven element—The part of an antenna that connects directly to the feed line.

Dummy load—Usually a resistor that is capable of dissipating the power from a transmitter. A dummy load is connected in place of an antenna, to allow a transmitter to operate at full power without radiating the output signal, and possibly causing interference.

Elevation angle—An angle measured in the vertical plane from the surface of the Earth. If most of the power from an antenna is radiated close to the surface of the Earth, we say the antenna has a low (elevation) angle of radiation. If most of the power is radiated directly up, we say the antenna has a high (elevation) angle of radiation.

Feed line (feeder)—See **Transmission line**.

Field strength meter—Usually consists of a detector such as a diode, and a meter. Used to measure the strength of a signal near the antenna.

Gain—One measure of the performance of an antenna, as compared with another antenna. Suppose the same transmitter is connected first to one antenna, and then to a second antenna, and the received signal strengths recorded at a remote location. The only thing that has changed is the transmitting antenna. The ratio of the received signal strengths is a measure of the gain of one antenna with respect to the other.

Gin pole—A pole or mast section used to help place an antenna on top of a tower.

Ground plane—Theoretically a very large, perfectly conducting surface. Most often, when an antenna requires a ground plane, the ground plane is replaced by the metal in a car body (for mobile work), or by **Radials** (see later) for stationary antennas.

Groundwave—A signal, usually on the lower HF bands, that follows the surface of the earth rather then going up toward the sky. See **Skywave**.

Guy wire—Wire used to hold the ends of antenna or keep a tower in place without swaying. Can be conductive or non-conductive, since their use is strictly structural and not electrical.

Half-wave dipole—A basic antenna used by radio amateurs. It consists of a length of wire or tubing, fed at the center. The entire antenna is $^1/_2$ wavelength long at the desired operating frequency.

Hop—Used to describe the path of a radio wave, as it goes from the antenna on the surface of the Earth to the ionosphere, and then back to the Earth. See **Skywave**.

Inverted V—One form of a dipole antenna. It is suspended from a single support at the middle, with the ends falling back toward the ground; thus the name comes from its inverted-V shape.

Ionized layers and Ionosphere—Bands of free electrons and ions at altitudes of 30 to 200 miles. They bend radio waves that hit them, returning some to earth.

Impedance—See **Characteristic impedance**.

Isotropic source—An imaginary antenna, located infinitely far from any other structure in free space. It is used as a standard for comparison of antenna gains. An isotropic source radiates equal signal strengths in all directions (a sphere).

Lightning arrestor—A device used to help keep the energy from a lightning strike from entering your shack by way of the antenna feed line.

Line of sight—VHF, UHF and microwave radio waves travel (propagate) just as light waves—in a straight line. This is called line-of-sight propagation.

Loading coil—A coil of wire, inserted in an antenna to make it appear *electrically* longer than its physical length. A mobile whip, used on the HF bands, often has a loading coil to make it appear $^1/_4$-wavelength long while still measuring only 8 feet long physically.

Lobes—See **Pattern**. The pattern of energy radiating from the front of a directional antenna is called the main lobe. Smaller, unwanted lobes (rear lobe, side lobe) describe the radiation from the rear and sides of an antenna.

Long-wire antenna—Strictly speaking, a single wire antenna, at least 2 or 3 wavelengths long. Often used to describe any *long* piece of wire or *random length* wire used as antenna.

Losses—A measure of how much energy is lost in a device. Most often, the losses depend on the frequency. A section of feed line (not designed for VHF) can have 5 or 10 times as much loss on the 2-m band as it has on the 80-m band.

Loop antenna—An antenna made as a complete polygon; round, square, triangular or with any number of sides. The loop can be a certain length, such as a full wavelength long, or it can be multiple turns around a smaller diameter.

Matching network—A device that matches one impedance level to another. For example, it may match the impedance of an antenna system to the impedance of a transmitter or receiver. See **Antenna tuners**.

Noise bridge—A test instrument used to measure antenna and transmission line impedances at various frequencies.

Omnidirectional—Describes an antenna that radiates equal signal strength in all compass (azimuth) directions.

Open-wire feed line—Parallel-conductor feed line with air as its primary insulation material.

Parallel-conductor feed line—Feed line with two conductors held a constant distance apart. Includes open-wire feed line, window line, TV twinlead and ladder line.

Patterns or Beam Shapes—A term used to describe a picture of how much energy is radiated from an antenna, when plotted against an axis of the antenna. Every antenna has a horizontal pattern and a vertical pattern.

Polarization—Describes the electrical-field characteristic of a radio wave. An antenna that is parallel to the surface of the earth, such as a dipole hung between two trees, produces horizontally polarized waves. One that is perpendicular to the earth's surface, such as a quarter-wave vertical, produces vertically polarized waves.

Propagation charts—Generally generated by a computer program, these charts predict what frequencies can be used successfully to contact one part of the world from another.

Pruning—Lengthening or shortening an antenna to change its characteristics and improve performance.

Quads—Generally similar to a **Yagi** antenna, with the same terminology and similar characteristics. The straight elements of a Yagi are replaced with continuous loops. The name "quad" is derived from the first designs, which used square (four-sided) loops.

Quarter-wavelength vertical antenna—An antenna constructed of a quarter-wavelength long radiating element placed perpendicular to the earth.

Radials—Wire elements used in place of a continuously conducting ground plane, usually for vertical antennas.

Radiating element—The portion(s) of an antenna that propagate transmitter energy into the air.

Reflector—An element behind the driven element in a Yagi and some other directional antennas.

Repeater—A station set up to receive at one (usually VHF or UHF) frequency and retransmit—or repeat—its input signal on another frequency. Thus it can hear low-power portable and mobile stations and retransmit their signals at a higher power with a better antenna. Two stations on VHF or UHF can use this *repeater mode*, or if they are within **Line of sight** they can communicate **Direct** without a repeater.

Resonant frequency—The desired operating frequency of a tuned circuit. At the resonant frequency of a half-wave dipole the feed-point impedance contains only resistance.

RF burn—A flesh burn usually caused by touching a conductor carrying RF energy. They tend to be very painful, even when tiny.

Rubber duck—Sometimes called a rubber ducky or just plain ducky. Usually a quarter-wave whip that is made smaller by helically winding the radiating element, and then encasing it in a flexible rubber or plastic cover.

S unit—A traditional way to measure received signal strength.

Skip—See **Skywave propagation**.

Skywave propagation—Describes RF energy radiated to the ionosphere (located in the sky!) and sent back to Earth. A radio wave traveling this path *skips* over the portion of the earth between the transmitting station and the point where the wave returns to earth, thus the term *skip*.

Sloper—A dipole configuration. One end is held in the air by a support and the other end slopes back toward the Earth.

Space and Free Space—When power leaves your antenna, we say it is radiated into space. Free space is a mathematical definition used in antenna design. In the early days of radio, *ether* was used to describe the imaginary "fluid" that conducted the radio waves.

Stacking, Stacked Antennas—Two or more antennas mounted one above the other or one next to the other to produce more gain.

Standing-wave ratio (SWR)—Sometimes called VSWR. A measure of the impedance match between the feed line and the antenna, feed line and the rig or feed line and the antenna tuner. VSWR is defined as the ratio of maximum voltage to minimum voltage along a feed line.

SWR meter or SWR bridge—A device used to measure SWR.

Transmission line—The wires or cable used to connect a transmitter or receiver to an antenna. Also called the *Feed line*. It comes in many physical forms, but the two most important characteristics of a feed line are its **Characteristic Impedance**—50-ohm line, 300-ohm line, 450-ohm line—and its **Losses**. The impedance usually does not vary with frequency but the losses do, increasing with increased frequency.

Traps—Inductors, capacitors and tuned circuits placed in radiating elements to allow their use on more than one band. For example, you can build or buy a *trap dipole* that has been designed to appear electrically as a single-band dipole on five different HF bands.

Vertical antenna—A antenna whose radiating element is vertical. Usually used with radials or some type of ground plane.

Wavelength—Often abbreviated λ (lambda). Higher frequencies have shorter wavelengths. Common lengths of antenna radiating elements are $1/4\ \lambda$ and $1/2\ \lambda$.

Yagi antenna—A popular type of amateur directional antenna. Often called a *beam antenna*. It has one driven element and one or more additional elements. It is usually rotated to provide coverage in different directions. See **Directors** and **Reflectors**.

About The American Radio Relay League

The seed for Amateur Radio was planted in the 1890s, when Guglielmo Marconi began his experiments in wireless telegraphy. Soon he was joined by dozens, then hundreds, of others who were enthusiastic about sending and receiving messages through the air—some with a commercial interest, but others solely out of a love for this new communications medium. The United States government began licensing Amateur Radio operators in 1912.

By 1914, there were thousands of Amateur Radio operators—hams—in the United States. Hiram Percy Maxim, a leading Hartford, Connecticut, inventor and industrialist saw the need for an organization to band together this fledgling group of radio experimenters. In May 1914 he founded the American Radio Relay League (ARRL) to meet that need.

Today ARRL, with more than 170,000 members, is the largest organization of radio amateurs in the United States. The League is a not-for-profit organization that:

• promotes interest in Amateur Radio communications and experimentation
• represents US radio amateurs in legislative matters, and
• maintains fraternalism and a high standard of conduct among Amateur Radio operators.

At League Headquarters in the Hartford suburb of Newington, the staff helps serve the needs of members. ARRL is also International Secretariat for the International Amateur Radio Union, which is made up of similar societies in more than 100 countries around the world.

ARRL publishes the monthly journal *QST*, as well as newsletters and many publications covering all aspects of

Amateur Radio. Its Headquarters station, W1AW, transmits bulletins of interest to radio amateurs and Morse Code practice sessions. The League also coordinates an extensive field organization, which includes volunteers who provide technical information for radio amateurs and public-service activities. ARRL also represents US amateurs with the Federal Communications Commission and other government agencies in the US and abroad.

Membership in ARRL means much more than receiving *QST* each month. In addition to the services already described, ARRL offers membership services on a personal level, such as the ARRL Volunteer Examiner Coordinator Program and a QSL bureau.

Full ARRL membership (available only to licensed radio amateurs) gives you a voice in how the affairs of the organization are governed. League policy is set by a Board of Directors (one from each of 15 Divisions). Each year, half of the ARRL Board of Directors stands for election by the full members they represent. The day-to-day operation of ARRL HQ is managed by an Executive Vice President and a Chief Financial Officer.

No matter what aspect of Amateur Radio attracts you, ARRL membership is relevant and important. There would be no Amateur Radio as we know it today were it not for the ARRL. We would be happy to welcome you as a member! (An Amateur Radio license is not required for Associate Membership.) For more information about ARRL and answers to any questions you may have about Amateur Radio, write or call:

ARRL Educational Activities Dept
225 Main Street
Newington, CT 06111-1494
(860) 594-0200
Prospective new amateurs call: 800-32-NEW-HAM
(800-326-3942)

Index

Y

JOIN ARRL TODAY AND RECEIVE A *FREE* BOOK!

I want to join ARRL. Send me the FREE book I have selected (choose one):

☐ *Repeater Directory*—gives you listings of more than 20,000 voice and digital repeaters throughout the US. ($7 value)

☐ *Your VHF Companion*—lets you explore the fascinating activities on the VHF bands: FM, repeaters, packet, CW, SSB, satellites, amateur television, and more. ($8 value)

☐ New Member   ☐ Previous Member   ☐ Renewal

_____

Call Sign (if any)   Class of License   Date of Birth

_____

Name

_____

Address

_____

City, State ZIP

Telephone Day ( )_____ Night ( )_____

Dues are $31 in US/$44 elsewhere (US funds). You do not need an Amateur Radio license to join. Individuals who are age 65 or over, upon submitting one-time proof of age, may request the dues rate of $25 in the US/$38 elsewhere (US funds). Immediate relatives of a member who receives *QST*, and reside at the same address may request family membership at $5 per year. Blind individuals may join without *QST* for $5 per year. If you are 21 or younger and a licensed amateur, a special rate may apply. Write to ARRL for details.

DUES ARE SUBJECT TO CHANGE WITHOUT NOTICE.

Payment Enclosed ☐

Charge to MC, VISA, AMEX, Discover No. _____

Expiration Date _____

Cardholder Name _____

Cardholder Signature _____

If you do not wish your name and address made available for non-ARRL related mailings please check this box ☐.

THE AMERICAN RADIO RELAY LEAGUE, INC
225 MAIN STREET NEWINGTON, CONNECTICUT 06111 USA
(860) 594-0200 YHAC 10/9
New Hams call (800) 326-3942